Nuffield Maths 2
Teachers' Handbook

# Nuffield Maths 5-11

# Nuffield Maths 2
# Teachers' Handbook
## National Curriculum Version

Published for the Nuffield-Chelsea Curriculum Trust Foundation by Longman Group UK Ltd

# Contents

Foreword by Geoffrey Matthews      iv

Introduction      v

## 1 Early stages of subtraction (N7)

**N7**: 1   Finding the difference      2
**N7**: 2   Counting back      4
**N7**: 3   Taking away      5
**N7**: 4   Recording subtraction      8
**N7**: 5   Practice sheets      10

## 2 A first look at place value (N8)

**N8**: 1   Early grouping activities and games      13
**N8**: 2   Grouping using cubes, etc.      16
**N8**: 3   Grouping in tens      21

## 3 Addition to 20 (N9)

**N9**: 1   Number bonds up to 20      30
**N9**: 2   Counting on      33
**N9**: 3   Ways of recording      36
**N9**: 4   Estimation of numbers up to 20      38

## 4 Subtraction involving numbers up to 20 (N10)

**N10**: 1   Difference by matching and counting      44
**N10**: 2   Subtraction by counting back      45
**N10**: 3   Taking away      46
**N10**: 4   Ways of recording      47

## 5 Introducing multiplication (N11)

**N11**: 1   Recognising and counting equivalent sets      52
**N11**: 2   Multiplication as repeated addition      53
**N11**: 3   Arrays and the commutative law      56
**N11**: 4   Activities and games for 'table facts' up to 30      59

## 6 Introducing division (N12)

**N12**: 1   The sharing aspect of division      66
**N12**: 2   The repeated subtraction aspect of division      67
**N12**: 3   Division as the inverse of multiplication      70
**N12**: 4   Remainders      72

### 7 Length (L2)

| | | |
|---|---|---:|
| **L2**: 1 | Appreciating the need for a standard measure | 75 |
| **L2**: 2 | Introduction of the metre | 75 |
| **L2**: 3 | Comparison with a 10 cm rod (decimetre) | 77 |
| **L2**: 4 | Measuring in centimetres—straight and curved lines | 78 |
| **L2**: 5 | Personal measurements in m and cm | 80 |

### 8 Shape and Space (S2)

| | | |
|---|---|---:|
| **S2**: 1 | Sorting for shape and size | 83 |
| **S2**: 2 | Fitting shapes together | 86 |
| **S2**: 3 | Surfaces and faces | 88 |
| **S2**: 4 | Covering surfaces—leading to area | 92 |
| **S2**: 5 | First ideas of symmetry | 96 |
| **S2**: 6 | Angles and rotation | 99 |

### 9 Weighing (W2)

| | | |
|---|---|---:|
| **W2**: 1 | Introduction of kilogram and $\frac{1}{2}$ kilogram | 108 |
| **W2**: 2 | Using the kilogram and $\frac{1}{2}$ kilogram | 110 |
| **W2**: 3 | Introduction of the 100 gram weight | 111 |

### 10 Time (T2)

| | | |
|---|---|---:|
| **T2**: 1 | Ways of measuring time | 117 |
| **T2**: 2 | Reading a dial | 118 |
| **T2**: 3 | Telling the time (hours, halves, quarters) | 121 |
| **T2**: 4 | Telling the time (five-minute intervals) | 124 |
| **T2**: 5 | Simple calculations involving time | 126 |
| **T2**: 6 | Other units of time | 127 |

### 11 Money (M2)

| | | |
|---|---|---:|
| **M2**: 1 | Reinforcement of coins up to 10p and introduction of 50p | 133 |
| **M2**: 2 | Breakdown of coins—equivalent values | 134 |
| **M2**: 3 | Making amounts up to 20p | 136 |
| **M2**: 4 | Addition—simple shopping bills | 138 |
| **M2**: 5 | Giving change and finding difference by counting on | 140 |
| **M2**: 6 | Subtraction by taking away | 141 |

### 12 Capacity (C2)

| | | |
|---|---|---:|
| **C2**: 1 | Introduction of the litre | 145 |
| **C2**: 2 | Comparing a litre with non-standard measure | 147 |
| **C2**: 3 | Introduction of $\frac{1}{2}$ litre and $\frac{1}{4}$ litre | 149 |
| **C2**: 4 | Cubes, boxes and walls | 150 |

### 13 The language of probability (P2)

| | | |
|---|---|---:|
| **P2**: 1 | Impossible, likely, certain | 154 |
| **P2**: 2 | How likely? | 156 |

| | |
|---|---:|
| **Index** | 159 |
| **Nuffield Maths 1 Teachers' Handbook Contents** | 160 |

# Foreword

I am very glad to have the opportunity of welcoming the 'National Curriculum version' of the Nuffield Mathematics 5–11 Project.

It is now a quarter of a century since the Nuffield Foundation launched its first primary mathematics project. This had the formidable task of re-thinking the whole subject and dragging it into the 20th century, away from the 'mechanical' sums and artificial 'problems' which had alienated generations of schoolchildren.

A landmark was the publication of 'Nuffield Mark II', starting in 1979. By then the innovations of the original project had been assimilated (and sometimes modified) and it was felt justified to produce pupils' materials for the first time.

'Nuffield' has maintained its momentum and remains the standard-bearer for curriculum development in primary mathematics. It is therefore not surprising that the National Curriculum reflects the Nuffield ideas regarding both content and method. Consequently the necessary changes from the previous edition of the Nuffield materials to accommodate the National Curriculum have been minimal.

The first Nuffield slogan was 'I do – and I understand'. It remains true that children learn through much practical work, and that no set of printed materials is a substitute for this. Indeed much mathematics will arise naturally within the framework of the whole curriculum (including of course science and English). However, reinforcement is essential and that is where the Nuffield publications come in.

Eric Albany and his team have ensured that 'Nuffield Maths' continues to set a standard of excellence in their provision of both teachers' and pupils' materials. It is indeed gratifying that the ideas so thoroughly explored and tested by Nuffield are now embedded in the National Curriculum.

Among the many institutions and people to whom the Foundation owes thanks for their help, I must especially acknowledge the part played by The Polytechnic, Wolverhampton in allowing the full-time secondment of Eric Albany to the project and also to the assistance given by Wolverhampton and Walsall Education Committees in providing accommodation and facilities for the project staff. We are extremely grateful to all those teachers and schools who have taken part in the trials of the materials. I would also like to express our thanks to Dieter Pevsner, Publications Manager of the project and his colleagues, and to our publishers, Longman Group Ltd, who have devoted so much effort and such skill to the editing, design and production of the materials.

Geoffrey Matthews

*Organiser of the first Nuffield Mathematics Teaching Project*
*Emeritus Professor of Mathematics Education,*
*King's College, University of London.*

# Introduction

*Nuffield Maths 5–11* is based on the original *Nuffield Mathematics Teaching Project* but revised in the light of experience, and extended to include the full range of pupils' materials in line with *Mathematics in the National Curriculum for England and Wales*.

The materials for rising 5 to 7 year olds are:
*Nuffield Maths 1 Teachers' Handbook* and expendable worksheets in booklet form (4½–6 year olds);
*Nuffield Maths 2 Teachers' Handbook* and expendable worksheets in booklet form (5½–7 year olds);
*Bronto Books*, Sets A, B, C, D and E – colourful books linking the extension of mathematical vocabulary with language development (4½–7 year olds);
*Early Challengers* – investigations suitable for young children.

The materials for 7–11 year olds are:
*Teachers' Handbooks 3, 4, 5, 6* and non-expendable pupils' books;
*Electronic Calculators*;
*Chellengers A, B, C and D*

For the sake of convenience, the teacher is referred to as 'she' and the pupil as 'he' throughout.

## Aims and objectives

The general aim of *Nuffield Maths 5–11 Project* is to promote understanding of the concepts and proficiency in the basic skills of mathematics in primary age children.

The objectives of the Teachers' Handbooks for *Nuffield Maths 1* and *2* are:

a) To give teachers clear guidance on the content, methods and timing appropriate at each stage of the course;
b) To give practical, 'down to earth' suggestions for teaching Number, Measurement, Shape and Data Handling, using activities suitable for children with a wide range of abilities and backgrounds;
c) To give ideas for making worksheets, workcards, charts, models, etc. and guidance in the use of both homemade and commercially available apparatus;
d) To stress the importance of the extension of mathematical vocabulary and cross-curricular links with reading, language development, science and the environment;
e) To suggest ways of dealing with children's difficulties.

## Using the materials

The materials of the *Nuffield Maths 5–11* Project can be used in a variety of classroom organizations including individual work, group teaching or class teaching. This should prove particularly useful to the teacher who tends to vary the type of organization to suit particular topics. Whichever system is used, it is important for teachers to remember the following points:

a) Children learn at different rates and so will not reach the same stage simultaneously;
b) Young children learn by doing and by discussion;
c) As well as finding out and 'discovering' things about mathematics, children need to be *told* things about mathematics, particularly if new vocabulary is involved.

The obvious line of development for a primary child learning mathematics would seem to be:

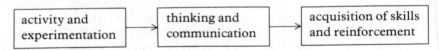

*Activity and experimentation* may vary from a child 'finding out by fiddling' to a structured or teacher-led activity.

*Thinking and communication* involves discussion, sometimes between children, sometimes between teacher and children. In the latter case, the teacher may pose a friendly 'I wonder' type of question to find out what the child is thinking—or indeed if the child is thinking at all. Talking leads to some sort of recording, the first introduction to which may be merely a placing or arranging of objects on a prepared sheet of card. Drawing and simple writing follow, leading to 'shorthand' and eventually to the use of symbols.

*Acquisition of skills and reinforcement* Apart from the obvious benefits of having certain useful skills and facts at one's fingertips, there is the question of building up confidence and enjoyment 'I can do these, Miss. Can I have some more?'

The important thing is that these three elements form a *sequence*. Worksheets provided by the Project are seen as part of the last element of the sequence. These are printed in four page leaflet form, with space for the date and pupils name. They should not be given to the children before they have had ample opportunity for activity, experimentation, thinking and discussion.

## Chapters and stages

This Handbook contains: six chapters on *Number* (labelled N7 to N12); one chapter on *Shape and Space* (S2); one chapter on *Money* (M2); one chapter on *Probability* (P2); and four chapters on *Measurement*: Length (L2), Time (T2), Capacity (C2), and Weighing (W2). These chapters develop and extend the topics begun in *Nuffield Maths 1 Teachers' Handbook*.

Each chapter is divided into stages which are also numbered. The second chapter on Weighing, for example, contains three stages which are labelled W2:1, W2:2 and W2:3. (See Contents for details of stages in each chapter.)

The chapters on Shape and Space, Measurement, Money and Probability need not be introduced in the order in which they appear in this Handbook. Indeed, the various stages are intended to run in parallel with the work on Number. A 'suggested order of development' is given on page viii.

Next to the full list of Contents on page ii and iii, there is a grid which teachers may wish to use as a record of the stages reached by groups or individual children.

# Chapter format

Each chapter of the *Nuffield Maths 1* and *2 Teachers' Handbooks* is set out as follows:

National Curriculum
Attainment Target 3: Level 2
Attainment Target 5: Level 2

**A National Curriculum reference**
A photocopy master of the National Curriculum record sheet is at the end of this handbook.

**1 For the teacher:**
A brief outline of what is being attempted in the chapter, where it is leading, and what should have been covered before starting.

**2 Summary of the stages:**
Setting out the stages contained within a chapter.

**3 Vocabulary**
A list of the words and phrases which the children will need to be able to use and understand if they are to appreciate and explore the ideas in each chapter. The teacher may wish to include some of these words and phrases in her work on language. See note on *Bronto Books*, page x.

**4 Equipment and apparatus**
The sort of materials such as boxes, containers, pots, sticks, pictures, sorting toys, buttons, counters, cubes, beads, string, sand, plasticine, etc. which the teacher may need to collect in advance.

**5 Working with the children**
Suggestions for introducing and developing each stage through discussion, teacher-led activities, games, etc.; hints for making workcards, charts, models, displays and simple apparatus; how to check-up, where necessary, that a child understands a particular stage.

The accompanying worksheets, published by the Project, are reproduced on a reduced scale at the end of each stage after the reminder '*Worksheets should not be introduced until children have had plenty of practical experience and opportunity for discussion.*'

**6 References and resources**
A list of books and commercially produced materials which are appropriate for the chapter. No commercially produced equipment is deemed essential but is suggested as a possible alternative to homemade or environmental materials. Occasionally the Teachers' Guides published by the original *Nuffield Foundation Mathematics Teaching Project* may be listed in this section. Although these guides are now out of print, they are to be found in libraries and schools and still make a valuable contribution to mathematics education.

# Suggested order of development

| Number | | Quantities and Shape | |
|---|---|---|---|
| **N7**: 1 | Finding the difference | **S2**: 1 | Sorting for shape and size |
| **N7**: 2 | Counting back | **S2**: 2 | Fitting shapes together |
| **N7**: 3 | Taking away | **M2**: 1 | Reinforcement of coins up to 10p and introduction of 50p |
| **N7**: 4 | Recording subtraction | **M2**: 2 | Breakdown of coins – equivalent value |
| **N7**: 5 | Practice sheets | **T2**: 1 | Ways of measuring time |
| | | | |
| **N8**: 1 | Early grouping activities and games | **T2**: 2 | Reading a dial |
| **N8**: 2 | Grouping using cubes, etc. | **S2**: 3 | Surfaces and faces |
| **N8**: 3 | Grouping in tens | **T2**: 3 | Telling the time (hours, $\frac{1}{2}$'s, $\frac{1}{4}$'s) |
| | | **S2**: 4 | Covering surfaces – leading to area |
| | | **P2**: 1 | Impossible, likely, certain |
| | | | |
| **N9**: 1 | Number bonds up to 20 | **M2**: 3 | Making amounts up to 20p |
| **N9**: 2 | Counting on | **M2**: 4 | Addition – simple shopping bills |
| **N9**: 3 | Ways of recording | **S2**: 5 | First ideas of symmetry |
| **N9**: 4 | Estimation of numbers up to 20 | **L2**: 1 | Appreciating the need for a standard measure |
| | | **L2**: 2 | Introduction of the metre |
| | | | |
| **N10**: 1 | Difference by matching and counting | **W2**: 1 | Introduction of kilogram and $\frac{1}{2}$ kilogram |
| **N10**: 2 | Subtraction by counting back | **W2**: 2 | Using the kilogram and $\frac{1}{2}$ kilogram |
| **N10**: 3 | Taking away | **M2**: 5 | Giving change and finding difference |
| **N10**: 4 | Ways of recording | **M2**: 6 | Subtraction of money (taking away) |
| | | **S2**: 6 | Angles and rotation |
| | | | |
| **N11**: 1 | Recognizing and counting equivalent sets | **T2**: 4 | Telling the time (5 minute intervals) |
| **N11**: 2 | Multiplication as repeated addition | **C2**: 1 | Introduction of the litre |
| **N11**: 3 | Arrays and the commutative law | **C2**: 2 | Comparing a litre with non-standard measures |
| **N11**: 4 | Activities and games for 'table facts' up to 30 | **C2**: 3 | Introduction of $\frac{1}{2}$ litre and $\frac{1}{4}$ litre |
| | | **L2**: 3 | Comparison with a 10 cm rod |
| | | **W2**: 3 | Introduction of 100 gram weight |
| | | **P2**: 2 | How likely? |
| | | | |
| **N12**: 1 | The sharing aspect of division | **L2**: 4 | Measuring in cm |
| **N12**: 2 | The repeated subtraction aspect of division | **L2**: 5 | Personal measurement in m and cm |
| **N12**: 3 | Division as the inverse of multiplication | **T2**: 5 | Simple calculations involving time |
| **N12**: 4 | Remainders | **T2**: 6 | Other units of time |
| | | **C2**: 4 | Cubes, boxes and walls |

# Some suggestions for classroom organisation

**How much time should be allowed for teaching maths in a busy primary day?**

The exact amount of time spent each day will depend on the individual school, and class teacher, but approximately one hour a day is recommended. This can be a timetabled maths session, or can be integrated amongst other subjects because so many mathematical ideas underlie much of the work done in other areas of the curriculum.

**How many children can work together at one time?**

Maths work can be attempted as a class, in groups, or on an individual basis. Each child should be allowed to work at his or her own rate as far as possible. There will be times when several children can be grouped together at one level in order to introduce a new topic, and it may be desirable sometimes for discussion between all the children and the teacher, followed by activities on an individual or group basis.

**How many activities do I need to make for each stage?**

For each stage suggested in the Teachers' Handbook, it is recommended that as many as possible of the activities are prepared. It is more practical if this can be done by several teachers joining together to have access to the materials, keeping at least one complete set for all the school.

Commercially produced materials should be carefully selected and housed in a clearly labelled box — only the required number of the object, say Unifix bricks, should be in the activity box. Where activities involve comparison between different objects, a selection of these should be kept together in a box or envelope. Home-made cards can be added to the sets of activities at each stage, teachers again sharing ideas. Storage of the games needed from each chapter could be in a supermarket carton, attractively decorated by the children. Make sure you return the games after use to the central store. Train the children to help in tidying up. Some teachers may want to duplicate some games to be kept in their own classrooms.

Your welfare assistant, if you have one, or any willing parents may help to make some activities. Use the margins of the Teachers' Handbook to jot down additional activities which would fit in with the stage being taught. It's useful to collect magazine pictures, etc. which may be cut out and stuck on card for activities. Wherever possible, cover the cards with adhesive clear film.

**How should I introduce the worksheets?**

This will depend on the child. The worksheets should not be introduced until the children have had plenty of practical experience and opportunity for discussion. Some of the earlier worksheets used with younger children will require some explanation and preparatory teaching. Some of the written language may not be within the vocabulary of some of the children. In these cases the teacher must ensure that the child can read the instructions. The written language is a guide to the discussion which could evolve between the child and the teacher, either before or after completion of the worksheet. Always try to ask the child to 'read' his activity to you. This may be an explanation of his work rather than actually reading the written words.

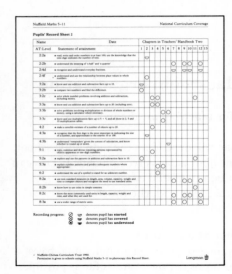

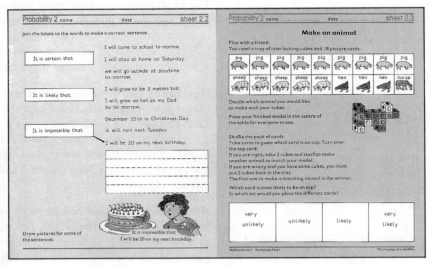

The worksheets are a useful check-up of the children's work and can be preserved as part of a class or school record. Each child's progress through the relevant levels of the National Curriculum can be shown by using the record sheet, a copymaster of which is at the back of this Teachers' Handbook.

# Bronto Books Sets A, B, C, D and E

The importance of discussion and the extension of mathematical vocabulary is emphasised by the Project's Bronto Books which are closely linked with Nuffield Maths 1 and 2.

Many Infant teachers maintain that few, if any, of the words and phrases used in mathematics are to be found in the early reading books. The brightly coloured Bronto Books were written specifically to fill this gap. They introduce the pre-school and infant child to mathematical language and concepts in an appealing and clear way using Bronto, an amiable brontosaurus, as a link man. In the back of each Bronto Book, suggestions for further activities extend the ideas presented and give additional practice in using and reading the vocabulary involved.

## Chapter 1
# Early stages of subtraction (N7)

National Curriculum
Attainment Target 3: Level 2
Attainment Target 5: Level 2

## For the teacher

This chapter introduces the early stages of subtraction through practical experiences involving finding the difference, movement on a number line ('counting back') and physical removal ('take away').

## Summary of the stages

**N7**: 1   Finding the difference

**N7**: 2   Counting back

**N7**: 3   Taking away

**N7**: 4   Recording subtraction by mapping, introduction of the symbol '—' and vertical subtraction

**N7**: 5   Practice sheets

## Vocabulary

More, less, find the difference, difference between, count back, take away, how many left?, leaves, subtract, subtraction.

## Equipment and apparatus

Rods or interlocking cubes or card strips (as used for addition), counters, beads, marbles, bricks, toy cars, boats, etc. Large pictures, suitably mounted, of 'John' and 'Peter', number lines, number rhymes involving counting backwards.

# Working with the children

### N7: 1  Finding the difference

In their earlier work whilst comparing two sets, children will have learned to establish which set has the greater number of members by using one-to-one correspondence. To find out exactly 'how many more' or 'how many less', they must count the unmatched members. This is made easier if the objects from the sets are lined up and 'paired off':

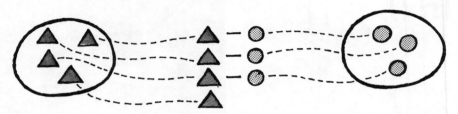

The difference is then apparent. At this stage practical situations mean far more to children than picture exercises. The word 'difference' may not be fully understood yet but a child may be able to observe in a real situation that, 'John has two more biscuits than Peter.' As the idea of difference is an important one, it should be carefully introduced. Situations should be structured using physical objects, which the child can line up and compare. The child should understand clearly which set has the greater number of members and be able to point out the difference before he begins to count how many unmatched members there are. An example might be:

'These are John's cars.' The teacher produces seven cars, all the same colour if possible.
'Here are Peter's cars.' The teacher places five cars of another colour alongside John's set of seven.
'Who has more cars, John or Peter?' The child may have to be shown how to match them, one-to-one. Once he has answered correctly, the teacher may say, 'Show me how many more cars John has than Peter.'
'How many is that? Count them.'
'Yes, John has two more than Peter.'
The teacher then builds up the idea that John has seven, Peter has five, and the difference between seven and five is two.

Children need plenty of time to practise problems similar to the one outlined. They need to handle actual objects, count and compare them and finally say what they have learned. When the teacher is sure that the child understands the meaning of 'difference', pictorial exercises may be introduced similar to:

Match. Draw a ring round the difference.

David has eight marbles.
Mark has five marbles.
The difference between 8 and 5 is  3

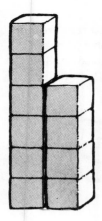

Later, rods or interlocking cubes may be used to illustrate the 'difference'. If commercially produced apparatus is not available, the strips used for addition serve as an alternative. The children may place the pieces side by side with the left-hand ends level or, in the case of rods, stand them upright side by side.

Notice that although it would be correct to say that the difference between 4 and 6 is 2, it is advisable at this stage, *to give the larger number first*. See the paragraph headed 'Subtraction is not commutative' on page 8.

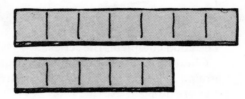

The difference between 6 and 4 is ☐.

The difference between 7 and 5 is ☐.

*Worksheets should not be introduced until children have had plenty of practical experience and opportunity for discussion.*

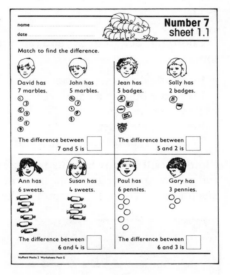

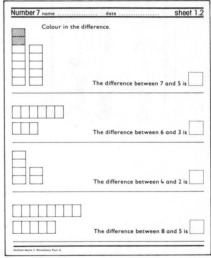

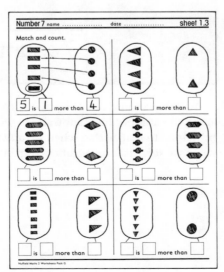

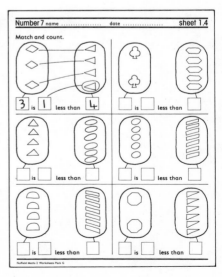

### N7:2   Counting back

Before we can expect children to subtract, we must check that they are able to count backwards from ten to one with facility. Children should be able to count back in ones starting first with 10, then 9, then 8 and so on. Short number sequences may be set up as exercises. These should have different starting points, with one number missing.

The child completes the series.

Children enjoy reciting number sequences by themselves and as part of a group. This may be practised often providing children understand what they are doing:
See *Counting Backwards*—Bronto Books Set A, Nuffield Mathematics 5–11.

Counting back from five and ten is included in the following children's songs:

Five little ducks set out one day.
Five little buns in a baker's shop.
Ten green bottles.
Five little chikadees.
Ten little sausages frying in a pan.

Children will already have had some experience of using the number line and counting on for addition; now they can count back along the number line for subtraction. For example, 'Put your finger on 7 and count back 3.'

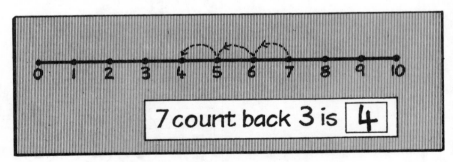

7 count back 3 is [4]

Addition should be connected with going on (i.e. moving forward →) along the number line; subtraction with going back (←). Children should be helped to realize that when we *add* two numbers, the result will be *more*; when we *subtract* one number from another, the result will be *less*.

*Worksheets should not be introduced until children have had plenty of practical experience and opportunity for discussion.*

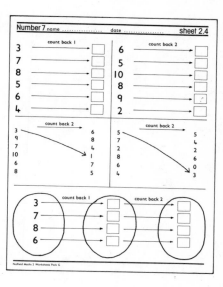

**Sheet 2.1**

name ...............
date ...............

**Number 7**
sheet 2.1

Say the numbers aloud to help you fill in the frames.

1  2  3  ☐  5  6  ☐  8

5  6  7  ☐  9  ☐

10  9  8  ☐  ☐  6  5  ☐  3

7  ☐  5  4  ☐  2  1

9  8  ☐  ☐  5  4  3

5  4  ☐  ☐  1

4  5  ☐  7  8  ☐  ☐

☐  9  8  ☐  ☐  5

Nuffield Maths 2 Worksheets Pack G

**Sheet 2.2**

Number 7 name ............... date ............... sheet 2.2

Subtract using a number line.

0  1  2  3  4  5  6  7  8  9  10

Put your pencil on 6.
Count back 2.                    6 count back 2 → 4

0  1  2  3  4  5  6  7  8  9  10

Put your pencil on 5.
Count back 2.                    5 count back 2 → ☐

0  1  2  3  4  5  6  7  8  9  10

Put your pencil on 9.
Count back 4.                    9 count back 4 → ☐

0  1  2  3  4  5  6  7  8  9  10

Put your pencil on 8.
Count back 6.                    8 count back 6 → ☐

Nuffield Maths 2 Worksheets Pack G

**Sheet 2.3**

Number 7 name ............... date ............... sheet 2.3

Subtract using a number line.

0  1  2  3  4  5  6  7  8  9  10

Put your pencil on 9.
Count back 6.                    9 count back 6 → ☐

0  1  2  3  4  5  6  7  8  9  10

Put your pencil on 10.
Count back 5.                    10 count back 5 → ☐

0  1  2  3  4  5  6  7  8  9  10

Put your pencil on 7.
Count back 2.                    7 count back 2 → ☐

0  1  2  3  4  5  6  7  8  9  10

Put your pencil on 3.
Count back 3.                    3 count back 3 → ☐

Nuffield Maths 2 Worksheets Pack G

**Sheet 2.4**

Number 7 name ............... date ............... sheet 2.4

| count back 1 | | count back 2 | |
|---|---|---|---|
| 3 → ☐ | | 6 → ☐ | |
| 7 → ☐ | | 5 → ☐ | |
| 8 → ☐ | | 10 → ☐ | |
| 5 → ☐ | | 8 → ☐ | |
| 6 → ☐ | | 9 → ☐ | |
| 4 → ☐ | | 2 → ☐ | |

count back 2                    count back 2

| 3 | 6 | 5 | 5 |
|---|---|---|---|
| 9 | 8 | 7 | 4 |
| 7 | 4 | 2 | 2 |
| 10 | 1 | 8 | 6 |
| 6 | 7 | 6 | 0 |
| 8 | 5 | 4 | 3 |

count back 1                    count back 2

| 3 | ☐ | ☐ |
| 7 | ☐ | ☐ |
| 8 | ☐ | ☐ |
| 6 | ☐ | ☐ |

Nuffield Maths 2 Worksheets Pack G

John     Anne

## N7 : 3   Taking away

'Take away' problems should be developed from a physical basis and presented to children in the form of real situations. For example, if the child has four crayons and his friend takes one away he has three left. This sort of situation is easily understood by young children. Many such stories can be presented and illustrated by the children using the following piece of apparatus.

Draw pictures of two children on a good sized piece of card and cover with clear *Contact*.

Collect sets of real objects, toy cars, boats, animals, coins, beads, bricks, marbles etc. or cut pictures of similar objects from old magazines and books, back with card and cover with clear *Contact*.

Begin by making up stories about the two children drawn on the card e.g. 'John had five boats.' Allow the child to place five boats on John's outline. 'John gave two boats to Anne.' Tell the child to take two boats away from John and give them to Anne. Ask the child how many boats

John has 6 cars.
He gives Anne 1 car.
John has ☐ cars left.
6 take away 1
         leaves ☐.

John has left. The teacher or the child should always conclude by describing in words what has happened. For example, 'John had five boats, he gave two to Anne, now John has three left.'

The children should be encouraged to invent their own examples of 'take aways' using the apparatus. Once the child has mastered the technique of taking away and counting what is left, then he may begin to use written problems with the apparatus and record his answers in long hand.

The teacher should fill in the spaces in the first and second lines indicating how many and what sort of object to use. The first and second frames on the fourth line should also be filled in by the teacher. When the child has demonstrated the take away problem and has filled in both the blank frames, he should read the whole card to the teacher.

During these exercises, by actually removing a number of objects from a given set, the children will begin to realize that it is not possible to take away a number of objects larger than in the original set. This is an important factor which when understood will avoid situations where the child says, 'five from three is two'.

It can also be shown that when the objects which were taken away are returned to their original set, then the number of objects in that set is the same as was started with. This helps to emphasize the relationship between addition and subtraction.

Addition involves 'putting together'; (composing) the 'take away' aspect of subtraction involves 'undoing' (decomposing).
For example:

    4 and 3 together make 7
    ⎧7 take away 4 leaves 3
    ⎩7 take away 3 leaves 4

Subtraction is seen as the opposite (or inverse) of addition.

Later as children begin to understand this relationship, they should be encouraged to use it to check their own calculations.

Eventually the apparatus may be replaced by 'pictorial take aways', and the child asked to write a number sentence to match the pictures.

5 take away ☐ ——leaves——→ ☐

A 'moving picture' approach to 'take away' requires very simple, home-made apparatus.

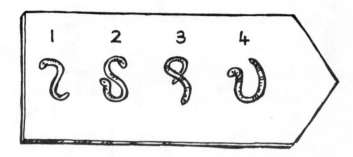

Remove the flap and cut a large envelope so that both ends are open.
Draw or stick a suitable picture from a magazine on the front of the envelope. (In the example the fish from *Animal Shapes* Bronto Books Set C is used.)

A worm is drawn below each of the numerals 1 to 4 on a stiff piece of card which is cut to a point at one end.

For the first instruction on the 'Worm Card', the child slides the pointed card into the envelope so that the fish 'eats' 3 worms. This leaves 1 worm, so the child writes the number sentence 4 take away 3 → 1 in his work book.

The same envelope may be used with other pointed cards and instruction cards up to 8.

Other similar envelopes and cards can be made for a dog eating bones, a cat eating fish, etc.

Picture problems and story problems should be used to help children link real situations with number sentences. Some children may not be able to cope with $8 - 2 \to \square$ but can arrive at the correct answer if the question is put in the form of a story. For example, 'If there are eight cows in a field and the farmer takes two away to market, how many are left?' Children should be encouraged to make up their own story problems related to number sentences:

'Tell me a story for $6 - 4 \to 2$'

Other children (and many adults!) can compute successfully but are stumped when presented with a written or verbal problem simply because they do not know how to extract the relevant information and translate it into the language of mathematics.

Every opportunity should be taken to relate simple picture or story problems with number sentences and vice versa. This will help the child who later might say, 'I can't do problems,' or 'Is it a times or a take away?'

*Worksheets should not be introduced until children have had plenty of practical experience and opportunity for discussion.*

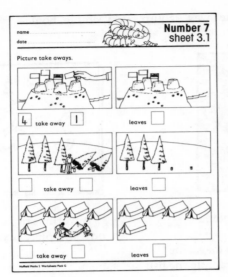

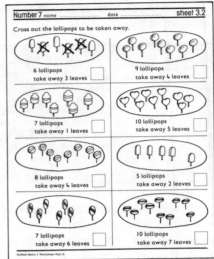

### N7: 4a   Introducing 'subtract' and the symbol ' − '

The word 'subtract' should be used before the symbol ' − ' and may be introduced as meaning 'take away' or 'find the difference' or 'count back'. Examples of mapping, similar to those outlined for addition may be used.

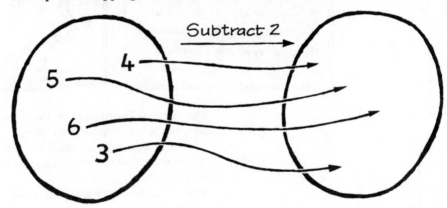

To work these, children usually begin by counting back in ones. This process, however, becomes very clumsy and inaccurate when, at a later stage, numbers are unwieldy e.g. 20 subtract 8 → □. Children should be encouraged to deal with number six, for example, in its own right rather than as a collection of six separate ones. Lots of written and oral work should be practised in counting on and back on the number line. Counting back in 2's, 3's, and 5's etc. will help reinforce number facts and simplify subtraction.

*Subtraction is not commutative*  In addition, order does not matter, e.g. 6 + 4 → 10 and 4 + 6 → 10. In subtraction, we must begin with the given amount and then write what has to be subtracted from it. It is important that children realize that 10 − 6 and 6 − 10 do not give the same result. Children should understand that when recording we begin with the larger number, although adults often confuse children by asking them to 'subtract 2 from 6'.

**In the early stages, it is better if word order in the language used matches the order of recording and operation.**

For example,

'Six take away two' or 'six subtract two'.

### N7: 4b Vertical subtraction

Like vertical addition this is introduced as just *another way of writing* subtraction problems. Children can begin by illustrating a subtraction example first as a sentence then in column form.

Children should be shown how to keep the numerals in line beneath each other and to place the sign in front of the number to be subtracted. Examples at this stage should be simple, dealing with numbers up to ten only. As always when introducing a new format or operation, it is advisable to use numbers well within the children's experience and understanding.

$$7 - 4 \rightarrow 3 \quad \text{or} \quad \begin{array}{r} 7 \\ -4 \\ \hline 3 \end{array}$$

*Worksheets should not be introduced until children have had plenty of practical experience and opportunity for discussion.*

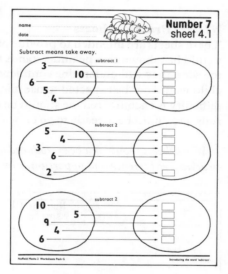

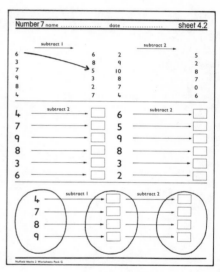

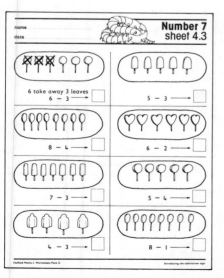

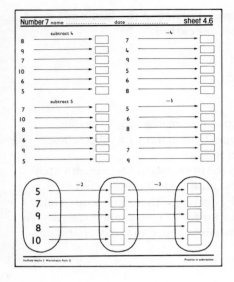

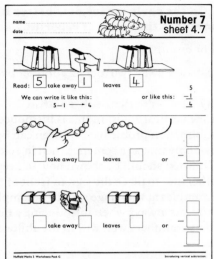

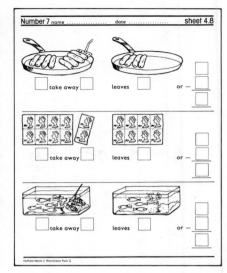

## N7 : 5    Practice sheets

These sheets are intended to provide practice and increase confidence once a child has shown that he understands the process involved. If introduced too soon they will undermine confidence and destroy incentive. Ideally, a child would not be expected to use materials as a support but, if a particular difficulty is encountered, he should be encouraged to make use of counters, rods, etc., until he is ready to go on without them.

*Worksheets should not be introduced until children have had plenty of practical experience and opportunity for discussion.*

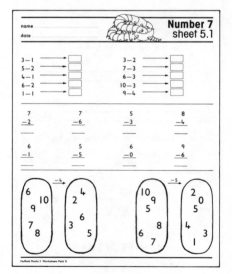

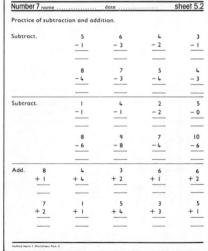

# References and resources

Burke, P. E. *Counting backwards*, Bronto Books Set A, Nuffield Maths 5–11, Longman Group UK Ltd 1979

Frobisher, B. and Gloyn, S. *Infants Learn Mathematics*, Ward Lock 1969

Matthews, G. and J. *Rhymes and Stories*, Early Mathematical Experiences Project, Longman Group UK Ltd Third Edition 1990

Nuffield Mathematics Teaching Project, *Mathematics Begins* ①, Nuffield Guide, Chambers/Murray 1967 (See Introduction, page vii)

Philip & Tacey, Rubber Stamp Number Lines, Subtraction Mapping Rubber Stamps

Pleuger, W. H. *Experiments with Structural Arithmetic in an English School, Guide to the Use of Stern Apparatus*, E. J. Arnold

Stone, R. S. *Multilink Manual*, E. J. Arnold

Taverner, N. *Unifix Teachers' Manual*, Philip & Tacey

# Chapter 2
# A first look at place value (N8)

National Curriculum
Attainment Target 2: Level 2
Attainment Target 2: Level 4
Attainment Target 4: Level 3

## For the teacher

This chapter deals with the introduction of two-digit numerals and the beginnings of place value. Place value is probably one of the most difficult concepts in our number system and many children become confused when two symbols which look alike have different values because of their relative positions. For example,

## 22

## This 2 does not have the same value as this 2.

Yet without the understanding of place value, the manipulation of numbers greater than ten cannot be attempted successfully. To some the idea of introducing place value to young children may seem inappropriate, but there are many grouping activities which, whilst reinforcing previous work on number, provide useful experience in preparation for fuller understanding of place value.

Since our number system is based on ten, why do we introduce games and activities using other bases? The trouble with base ten is a physical one. The child has to handle larger amounts of apparatus and is unable 'to see the wood for the trees'—or in this case, he is unable 'to see the structure for the cubes'. In working with bases 3, 4 or 5, the child can experience place value by using numbers he can manipulate easily and without having to cope with large amounts of material.

It must be stressed that, at this stage, the children are not 'doing bases'. They are not carrying out computations in multibase arithmetic; they are gaining valuable experience leading to the concept of place value by grouping, exchanging and positioning materials.

Before beginning the activities in this chapter, children should be able to

left | middle | right
a row

count up to ten by using one-to-one correspondence between a set of objects and the set of numerals from 0 to 10. The children will also need to be able to select the correct word to describe the position of a figure in a row.

## Summary of the stages

N8: 1 Early grouping activities and games

N8: 2 Grouping using cubes, etc.

N8: 3 Grouping in tens

## Vocabulary

Right, left, middle, are worth, bundle, longs, units, exchange, abacus, eleven, twelve, thirteen, fourteen, fifteen, sixteen, seventeen, eighteen, nineteen, twenty.

## Equipment and apparatus

Egg boxes, cubes, counters, sticks or rods.

For the games the following are required (instructions for making them are included in the description of the game): fish, nets, boats, windows, houses.

## Working with the children

### N8: 1   Early grouping activities and games

In the first instance familiar things are used to give children practical experience in collecting or grouping objects into sets.

For example:

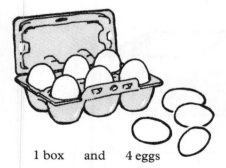

1 box   and   4 eggs

2 trays   and    2 cakes

Children present today:
3 full tables and 4 children.
(It is better not to
refer to the four as 'odd' children.)

Using pegs and pegboard:
3 rows and 2 pegs.

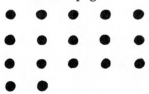

At this stage there is no question of counting the total and the only recording done would be in the form of a sentence written by the teacher *after* discussion. The point being made here is that a numeral may refer to different things depending upon its position—the numeral on the left giving the number of sets or groups; the numeral on the right giving the number of 'units' or 'left overs' not put into full sets. Thus, in the egg example, 1 boxful and 4 eggs, the 1 is worth more because it means a full box. In the cake example, 2 trays and 2 cakes; the first 2 on the left is worth more than the 2 on the right.

The children themselves may be used as the elements being grouped. For example, with 14 children the teacher could say, 'Make rings of four' to give 3 rings and 2 children, or 'Make rings of five' to give 2 rings and 4 children. In this case it would also be important to say, 'Make rings of seven' to give 2 rings and 0 children, stressing that the zero meant that there were no children 'over'.

*The fish game—grouping in threes*

Materials needed (drawn half-size):

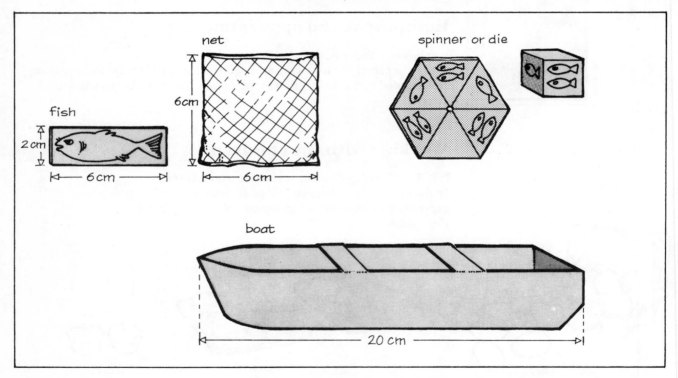

The fish are made from medium card or thin plastic—6 cm by 2 cm (20 required).
The nets are clear polythene bags just large enough to take 3 fish (6 cm by 6 cm). Lines are drawn on the polythene bags to make them look like nets (8 required).
The boats are made from card, just long enough to take 3 nets (2 required). [See Appendix 1 to this chapter for pattern.]
A spinner is cut from card; or a cube, with its faces marked in the same way as the sections of the spinner, may be used as a die.

A flat board is made from manilla ruled and headed:

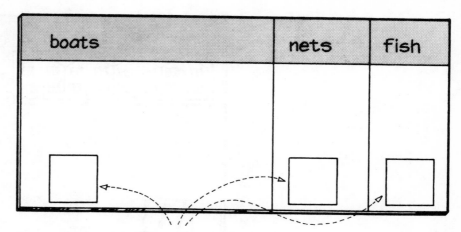

Frames, in which children will insert numerals later.

The game is played by two children taking it in turn to spin (or to roll the die) and putting out the score obtained in fish. Whenever 3 fish are collected they are put into a net and the net is then placed in the correct column. Three full nets are loaded into a boat and the boat placed in the 'boats' column. The game need not be competitive, although children often point to a net and say, 'That one's mine.' The game ends when two full boats have been built up.

From time to time, the teacher may ask the children to put the appropriate numerals (0, 1 or 2) in the frames provided.

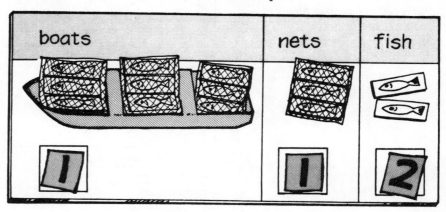

'1 boat                    1 net        2 fish'

From this, discussion can follow on the *position* of the numerals and *what they stand for*. 'The 1 on the left means 1 boat; the 1 in the middle means 1 net; the 2 on the right means 2 fish.'

The principle of exchange should also be discussed in simple terms. 'Three fish make a netful; three nets make a boatful.'

*The house game—grouping in fours* Windows, houses and streets are made from card or felt and are placed on a flat board made from manilla. This time the sections of the spinner or the faces of the die are marked in 'windows':

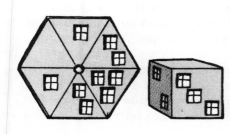

See Appendix 2 for pattern.

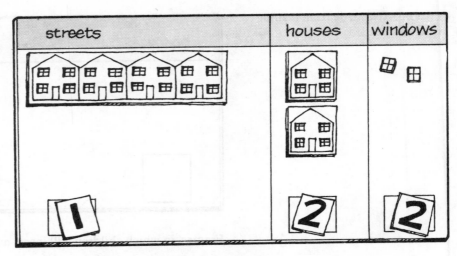

The game is played as before but with 4 windows making a house, 4 houses a street, until 3 streets are built up.

Other similar games can be made using simple, home-made apparatus. For example:

5 petals make a flower; 5 flowers a garland;
6 cherries on a cake; 6 cakes in a tray; etc.

*Worksheets should not be introduced until children have had plenty of practical experience and opportunity for discussion.*

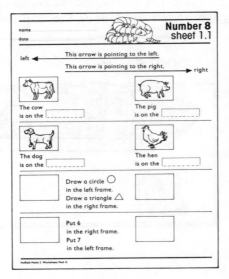

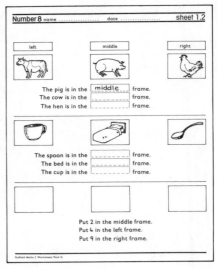

### N8: 2  Grouping with sticks, cubes, etc.

Once children have had plenty of practice with the grouping activities and games and can place pieces in the correct columns on the board, they may be ready for an approach slightly more formal but still using apparatus. At this stage, the emphasis will continue to be on grouping, placing and, eventually, recording in columns.

Games similar to the 'fish' and 'houses' games can now be played using spinners or dice marked in dots or 'units'. The pieces are set out on a board divided into headed columns. It is advisable to produce a few 'zero cards' for placing in the second or third columns where necessary.

The children should be encouraged to use language such as: 'Three units make a long and the longs are put in this column.' 'Four of these in this column make one of those in that column.' 'The bigger ones go on the left and the smaller ones go on the right.' 'That 2 stands for two longs; that 3 stands for three units.' 'The 0 means there are none of those.'

Once recording starts, it is important that the children learn to read the numerals figure by figure. For example, 13 should be read as 'one three', not as 'thirteen' because 'thirteen' means 'a group of *ten* and three units'.

A variety of apparatus, either commercially manufactured or homemade, can be used.

Here are a few examples:

*Using sticks as units*
The teacher uses stiff card
to make boards similar to:

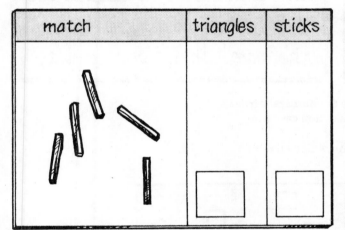

Grouping in threes.                                     Grouping in fours.

The children are asked to match sticks to the pictures *without counting*. They then rearrange the sticks to make triangles or diamonds placing them and the sticks left over in the correct columns. The correct numeral cards are put in the frames (just as in the 'fish' and 'house' games) and the result read to the teacher, figure by figure.

'One diamond and three sticks.'
The word 'diamond' is preferred here as 'square' will be used later for the heading of a third column.

*Using Centicubes, Multilink, Metricubes or Unifix*
Unit cubes are matched to the coloured squares on the board and separate
instructions written on long pieces of card. Each board can be used with
several instructions.

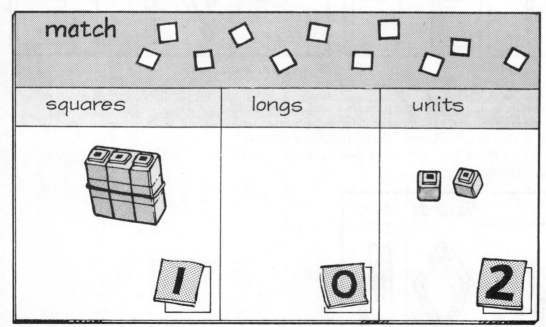

Examples of instruction cards:

When I match and group in 3's
there are ☐ longs and ☐ units.

When I match and group in 4's
there are ☐ longs and ☐ units.

The child carries out the matching and grouping, puts the numeral cards
in the frames on the board and copies the completed instruction card into
his work book.

This activity may be extended to include a third column which enables a
further grouping of 'longs' into 'squares'.

| match | | |
| --- | --- | --- |
| squares | longs | units |
| [1] | [0] | [2] |

'One square,
no longs
and two units'.

The advantage of this type of material is that the units can be actually
joined together to make a group of 3, 4, 5, etc., in the form of a 'long'.
Later, 'longs' can be grouped into 'squares'. Centicubes, Multilink and
Metricubes can be joined to form 'squares'. Unifix supply plastic retaining
frames for constructing 'squares'.

*Using Stern, Cuisenaire, Colour Factor*
In this case, if grouping in fours for example, four unit cubes would be
exchanged for a 4-rod and four 4-rods banded together to make a square.

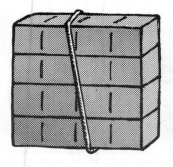
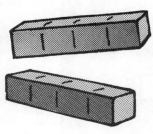
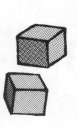

| squares | longs | units |
|---------|-------|-------|
| 1 | 2 | 2 |

*Using Multibase Material*
Materials specially designed to show place value such as Dienes' Multibase
Arithmetic Blocks (E.S.A), Tillich Blocks (Arnold), or Multibase Blocks
(Metric Aids).

Grouping in fives

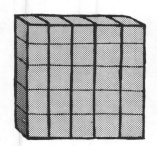

| squares | longs | units |
|---------|-------|-------|
| 1 | 2 | 4 |

*Home-made Multibase Kit, using card*
Rule up a piece of card in 1 centimetre squares or paste 1 cm squared
paper on to card. Cut out 'squares', 'longs', 'units', etc. as required.

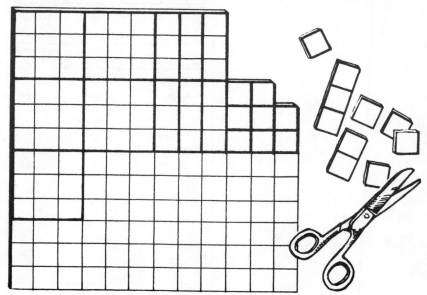

Grouping, exchanging and recording would be as in previous examples.

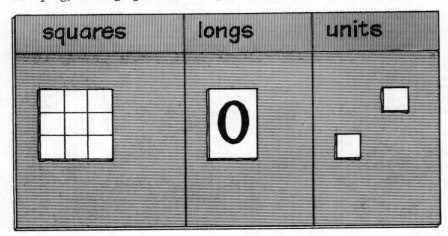

The 'zero card'
placed in the 'longs' column
reminds the child to record
this situation as

| squares | longs | units |
|---------|-------|-------|
| 1 | 0 | 2 |

instead of

| squares | longs | units |
|---------|-------|-------|
| 1 | | 2 |

*Worksheets should not be introduced until children have had plenty of practical experience and opportunity for discussion.*

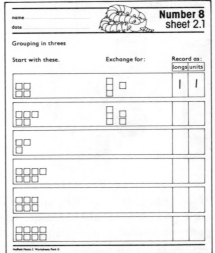

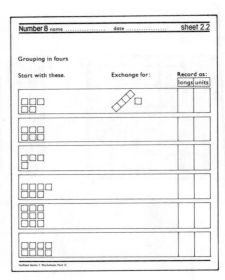

## N8 : 3   Grouping in tens

The activities in the two preceding stages were planned in order to lead children to appreciate the importance of the *position* of numerals. The children have built up numerals consisting of two or more digits without being overwhelmed by a large amount of material. As they become more confident at 'reading' these numerals—that is, not only interpreting each digit but also its position—they will be ready to apply this experience to our number system which groups in tens. In other words, we want the children to transfer their experience
of this situation :                                            to this :

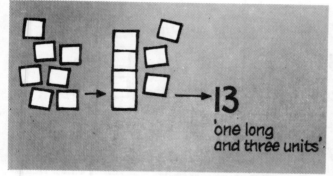

'one long
and three units'

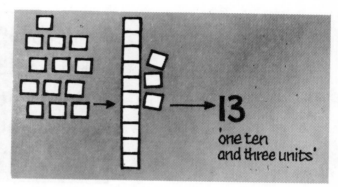

'one ten
and three units'

We can then talk about the number system we use everyday, based on tens, and introduce the special names we give to numerals in this system,—eleven, twelve, thirteen, etc. The importance of ten can be stressed by making a 'bundle' of straws, sticks etc., using elastic bands or pipe cleaners.

*Counting board activity*  For this activity the teacher draws the outline of a ten-rod and nine units and a numeral frame on a piece of stiff card.

If interlocking cubes (Centicubes, Multilink, Metricubes, Unifix, etc.) are to be used, the ten-space is drawn just large enough for a 'stick' of ten cubes. In this case it is probably better to use one particular colour for the 'ten-stick'.

A 10-card is made just large enough to fit the numeral frame and single digit cards from 1 to 9 are made half this size—that is large enough to cover the zero of the ten.

For the first stage of the activity,
the children use an instruction card like this :

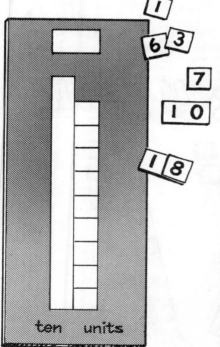

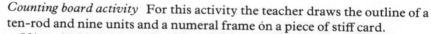

| | | |
|---|---|---|
| Put out 1 ten and 4 units | 10 + 4 → ☐ |
| Put out 1 ten and 9 units | 10 + 9 → ☐ |
| Put out 1 ten and 3 units | 10 + 3 → ☐ |
| Put out 1 ten and 2 units | 10 + 2 → ☐ |
| Put out 1 ten and 6 units | 10 + 6 → ☐ |

| 1 0 | 4 | 1 0 | 1 4 |

As the child puts out the ten-rod or ten-stick, he places the numeral $\boxed{10}$ in the numeral frame. As he puts out the four single cubes in the 'unit' spaces, he places the numeral $\boxed{4}$ on top of the $\boxed{10}$ so that the zero is covered and $\boxed{1\,4}$ is seen. The child then writes $10 + 4 \rightarrow 14$ in his work book.

For the second stage of the activity the process is reversed using an instruction card like this:

Put out 15.     15 is ☐ ten and ☐ units.
Put out 13.     13 is ☐ ten and ☐ units.
Put out 16.     16 is ☐ ten and ☐ units.
Put out 14.     14 is ☐ ten and ☐ units.
Put out 17.     17 is ☐ ten and ☐ units.

Unifix materials include a *1-ten and units tray* and *ten and units number cards* which can be used for a similar activity.

It is important that children become thoroughly familiar with the appearance of the numerals from 11 to 20 as they set the pattern for all the decades that follow. The extension of the number line to 20 and possibly beyond will help to establish this pattern, especially if material is set out too.

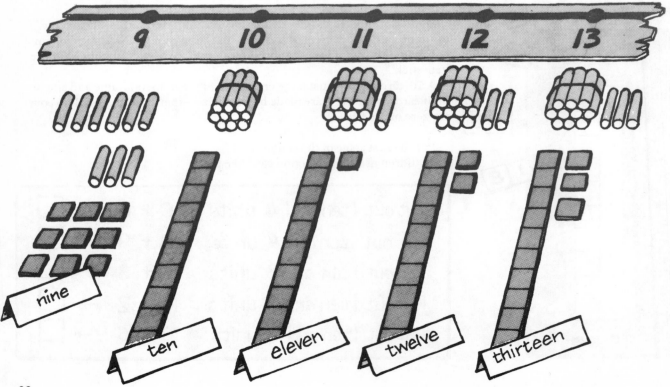

### Number line activity

2-centimetre graph paper is cut into strips 2 squares wide. The teacher cuts a strip to the required length and begins to label the intervals. The child completes the labelling and the strip is then ready for use in conjunction with Worksheet N8 : 3.6.

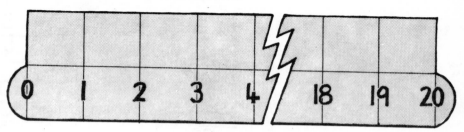

Early activities such as counting on in twos and threes etc. can also be practiced on the number line—possibly using different coloured pencils.

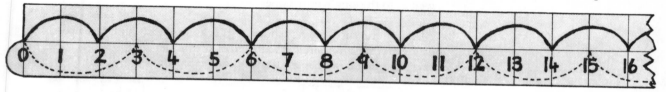

It is also important that the children learn to connect the sound with the appearance of the numerals, especially as it sounds as though we say those from thirteen to nineteen the wrong way round. Logically, 16 ought to be called 'teen-six' or 'onety-six'! Many children find this very confusing and they tend to write seventeen, for example, as '71' because the 'seven' part is sounded first.

The connection between bundles of ten and numerals in both figure and word form can be reinforced by playing a game using dominoes made from card.

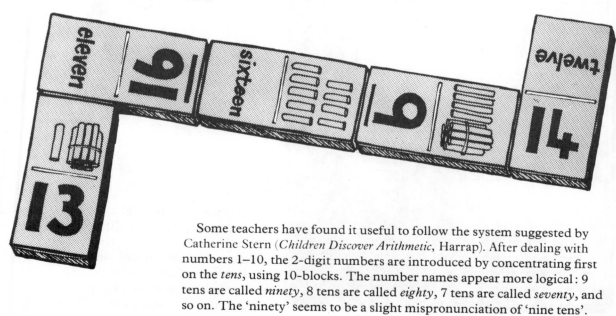

Some teachers have found it useful to follow the system suggested by Catherine Stern (*Children Discover Arithmetic*, Harrap). After dealing with numbers 1–10, the 2-digit numbers are introduced by concentrating first on the *tens*, using 10-blocks. The number names appear more logical: 9 tens are called *ninety*, 8 tens are called *eighty*, 7 tens are called *seventy*, and so on. The 'ninety' seems to be a slight mispronunciation of 'nine tens'.

Using ten-blocks in place of unit cubes, the transfer is made to adding in full tens:
"2 and 3 is 5, so 2 tens and 3 tens are 5 tens.
This leads to recording:

$$
\begin{array}{r} 2 \\ + 3 \\ \hline 5 \end{array}
\qquad
\begin{array}{r} 1 \\ + 3 \\ \hline 4 \end{array}
\qquad
\begin{array}{r} 5 \\ + 4 \\ \hline 9 \end{array}
$$

$$
\begin{array}{r} 20 \\ + 30 \\ \hline 50 \end{array}
\qquad
\begin{array}{r} 10 \\ + 30 \\ \hline 40 \end{array}
\qquad
\begin{array}{r} 50 \\ + 40 \\ \hline 90 \end{array}
$$

Emphasise that number facts such as $2 + 3 = 5$ apply to the 10-blocks as well as to the single unit-cubes.

A numeral card-holder, some 10-blocks and unit-cubes are used to establish that a numeral on the *right* of the holder means single cubes or *ones*; a numeral on the *left* of the holder means *tens*.

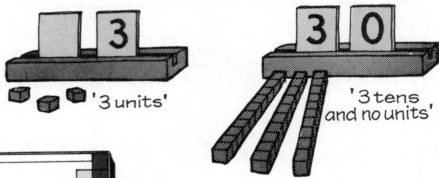

'3 units'

'3 tens and no units'

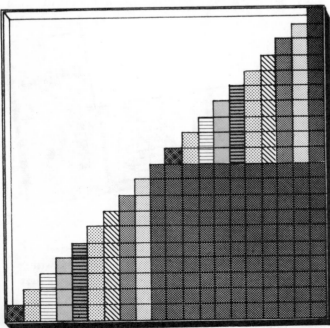

Then the series from 11 to 20 is presented as a continuation of the 1–10 staircase using $(10 + 1)$, $(10 + 2)$, ... etc. As soon as the child understands the structure of the 'teen' numbers, the symbols are introduced so that 17, for example, is seen as 1 ten and 7 units.

*Worksheets should not be introduced until children have had plenty of practical experience and opportunity for discussion.*

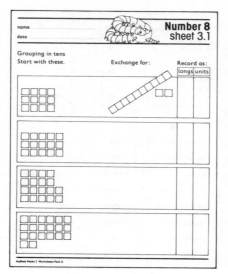

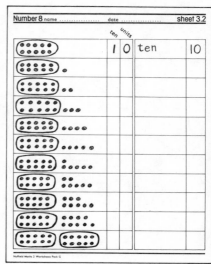

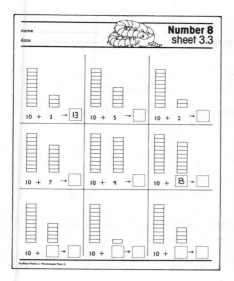

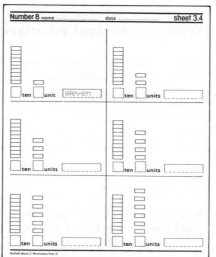

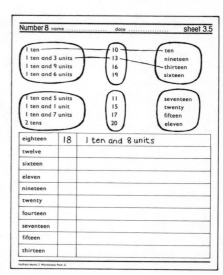

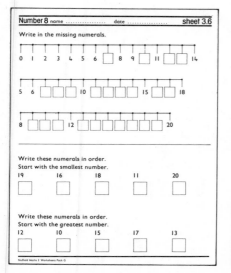

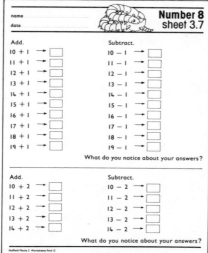

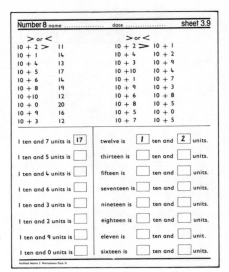

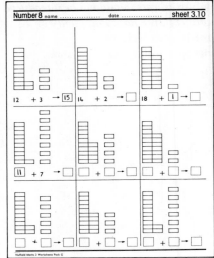

## References and resources

Burke, P. *Left, right*, Bronto Books Set B, Burke, P. and Albany, E. *Tally Bronto* Set E, Nuffield Maths 5–11, Longman Group UK Ltd 1979

Shuard, H. and Williams, E. M. *Primary Mathematics Today*, Longman Group UK Ltd 1976

E. J. Arnold, *Tillich Blocks, Multilink*

Nicolas Burdett Ltd, *Multibase Blocks*

Osmiroid, *Centicubes*

Philip and Tacey Ltd, *Unifix Cubes, Unifix Retaining Frames, Unifix-Ten and Units Tray, Unifix Ten and Units Number Cards*

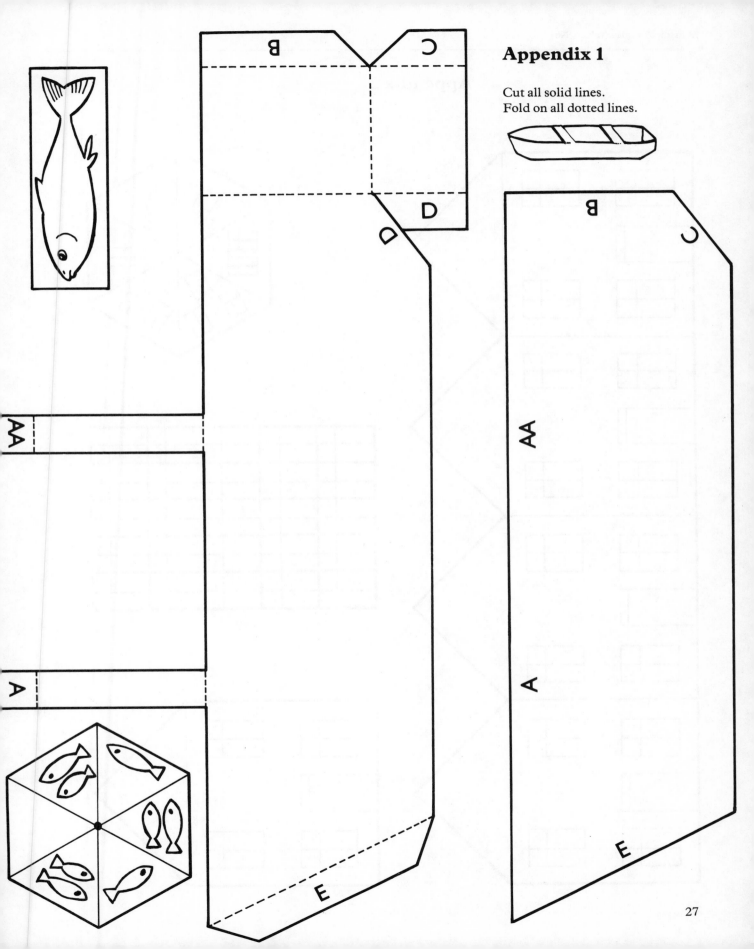

## Appendix 1

Cut all solid lines.
Fold on all dotted lines.

B

C

D

D

AA

A

E

B

C

AA

A

E

27

# Appendix 2

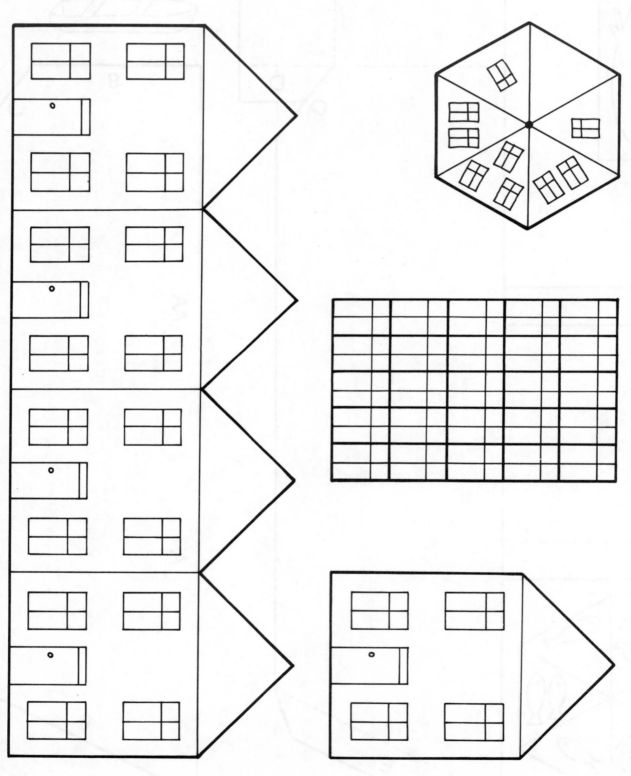

# Chapter 3
# Addition to 20 (N9)

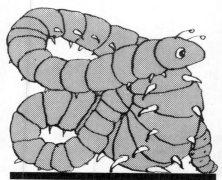

National Curriculum
Attainment Target 3: Level 2
Attainment Target 3: Level 3
Attainment Target 4: Level 2
Attainment Target 5: Level 1

## For the teacher

This chapter deals with addition of numbers up to 20. It links the previous work on numbers up to 10 (Chapters 5 and 6 of *Teachers' Handbook 1*) with the introduction of two-digit numerals and the beginnings of place value (Chapter 2 of this Handbook).

At this stage, there will be no attempt to establish a formal approach to addition involving re-grouping (that is, we shall not be 'carrying').

| Addition is developed by: | Examples |
|---|---|
| 1 reinforcing and extending number bonds already used. | $4 + 2 = 6$<br>so $14 + 2 = 16$ |
| 2 remembering 'You can add forwards or backwards.'<br>(Addition is commutative.) | $3 + 10 = 10 + 3 = 13$ |
| 3 realizing that, 'You can add in any order you like.'<br>(Addition is associative.) | $(5 + 3) + 7 = 5 + (3 + 7)$<br>$= 5 + 10$<br>$= 15$ |

4 counting on using a number or number strip

⊕ →

9 count on 4 → 13

5 recognizing patterns in addition.

$1 + 4 = 5$
$11 + 4 = 15$
$21 + 4 = 25$ etc.

This would also seem a good time to introduce ' = ', the sign of equality. One of the reasons for delaying the introduction of = is that when it is employed in connection with things or words rather than numerals, all

29

sorts of inaccuracies and abuses tend to arise. This is dealt with at greater length in a special note on 'The use of =' in the Appendix to this chapter. However, it would be wrong to make too much of the introduction of the '=' sign to children; it should be brought in as another way of recording statements about numbers.

## Summary of the stages

**N9**: 1  Number bonds up to 20

**N9**: 2  Counting on

**N9**: 3  Ways of recording

**N9**: 4  Estimation of numbers up to 20

## Vocabulary

add, plus, total, altogether, is as many as, is the same number as, can be written as, equals, estimate, estimation, nearly, about, roughly, almost, close to, a bit under/over, just under/over.

## Equipment and apparatus

Counters, beads, buttons, cubes, rods, etc. Stern, Unifix, Cuisenaire, Colour Factor, Centicubes, Multilink or Metricubes, etc., paper plates, 1p, 2p and 10p coins.

## Working with the children

### N9: 1  Number bonds up to 20

The prospect of trying to get children to remember all the possible combinations of numbers which give totals up to twenty may seem daunting. However, if we approach the task systematically, using practical aids, building on what is known and gradually extending the experience and knowledge of the children, they will increase their facility with numbers. It must be remembered that this new knowledge and facility will only be retained if opportunities are given for practice and reinforcement—preferably in short, regular 'doses'. (Those odd five-minute sessions, for example.)

One possible line of development is:

1  Reinforce number bonds up to 10, not forgetting the zeros and being sure to remind children about 'backwards and forwards'

i.e. $7 + 2 \rightarrow 9$ and $2 + 7 \rightarrow 9$.

Whilst doing this, the '=' sign can be introduced—but see note in the Appendix to this chapter.

2  Reinforce 'the teens', again adding both ways.
For example,

$10 + 4 = 14, \quad 3 + 10 = 13$, etc.

3  Now combine 1 and 2 by getting children to see that the order of addition does not matter. For example,

$$10 + \ 3 + 2 = 10 + 5 = 15$$

$$3 + 10 + 2 = 10 + 5 = 15$$

$$6 + 10 + 3 = 10 + 9 = 19$$

4  Now the set of 'teen-and-singles' which give a total of 20 or less. For example,

| | |
|---|---|
| $11 + 3 = 14$ | $13 + 4 = 17$ |
| $16 + 2 = 18$ | $19 + 1 = 20$, etc. |

These cases are based on 1, 2 and 3 above.

5  Encourage children to 'spot pairs that make 10'. For example,

$$3 + 6 + 7 = 10 + 6 = 16$$
'3 and 7 is 10; and 6 makes 16'
  is easier than
'3 and 6 is 9; and 7 makes 16'

6  Pairs of single-digit numbers which give totals from 11 to 18. Again, the commutative property of addition halves the number of cases. The pattern is important:

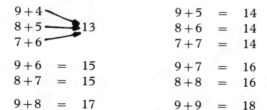

| | | | | | |
|---|---|---|---|---|---|
| $9 + 6$ | $=$ | $15$ | $9 + 7$ | $=$ | $16$ |
| $8 + 7$ | $=$ | $15$ | $8 + 8$ | $=$ | $16$ |
| $9 + 8$ | $=$ | $17$ | $9 + 9$ | $=$ | $18$ |

Notice the last row for each of the even 'teens' in the right hand column.

7  Other triples of single digit numbers which give totals of 20 or less

$$8 + 3 + 4 = 11 + 4 = 15$$
$$9 + 7 + 2 = 16 + 2 = 18$$

Most of these are covered by 6 and 4 above.

Using this system, the only facts which are completely 'new' to the children are those in 6. The methods described in Chapters 5 and 6 of *Nuffield Maths 1 Teachers' Handbook*, using structural apparatus such as Stern, Multilink, Cuisenaire, Colour Factor, Unifix, Metricubes, Centicubes, etc., can all be adapted for use with number bonds up to 20.

Ways of making 14.

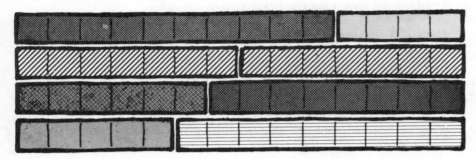

10 + 4

7 + 7

6 + 8

5 + 9

etc.

If no commercially produced apparatus is available, cardboard strips or squared paper make good substitutes.

Off-cuts from squared paper are useful for making addition rectangles:

| + | 5 | 6 | 7 | 8 | 9 | 10 | 11 |
|---|---|---|---|---|---|----|----|
| 5 | 10 | | | | | | |
| 6 | | | | | | | 17 |
| 7 | | | | 15 | | | |
| 8 | | 14 | | | | | |

| + | 13 | 11 | 10 | 12 | |
|---|----|----|----|----|---|
| 7 | 20 | | | | |
| 2 | | | | | |
| 1 | | | 11 | | |
| 5 | | | | | |
| 6 | | 17 | | | |
| 4 | | | | | |

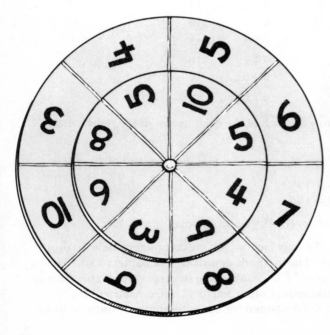

'Moving Targets' are very popular with children. Two circles are cut from stiff card, one with 5 cm diameter the other 8 cm. The circles are divided into eight sectors or 'slices' and fixed together with a brass paper fastener. Numerals are written in the spaces so that when the 'spokes' are lined up, eight addition problems are given:

10 + 5 = 15
5 + 6 = 11
4 + 7 = 11
9 + 8 = 17, etc.

When the inner circle is moved round, another eight addition problems appear, and so on.

The Triple Dice Game provides practice at adding three single-digit numbers to give totals from 3 to 18 (Worksheet N9: 1.6).

*Worksheets should not be introduced until children have had plenty of practical experience and opportunity for discussion.*

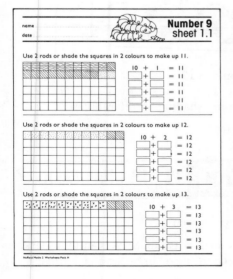

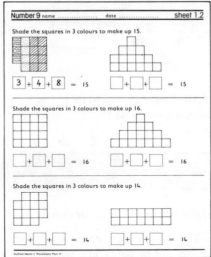

Number 9 name .......... date .......... sheet 1.3

Shade the squares in three colours to make up 17.

☐ + ☐ + ☐ = 17     ☐ + ☐ + ☐ = 17

Shade the squares in 3 colours to make up 19.

☐ + ☐ + ☐ = 19     ☐ + ☐ + ☐ = 19

Shade the squares in 3 colours to make up 18.

☐ + ☐ + ☐ = 18     ☐ + ☐ + ☐ = 18

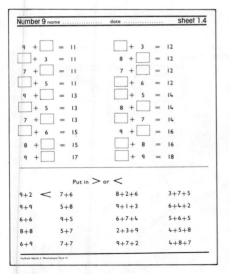

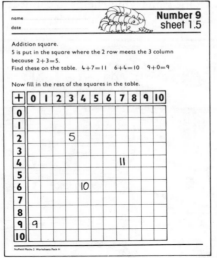

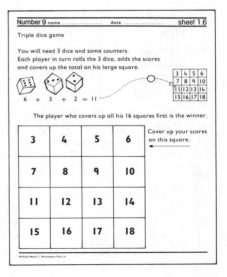

## N9 : 2   Counting on
Activities using either :

the number *line*

or the number *strip*

described in Chapter 6 of *Nuffield Maths 1 Teachers' Handbook*, can now be extended to include numbers up to 20.

Sometimes a child encounters difficulty when counting on because he taps his finger on the starting point or square and counts 'one'. One way to overcome this is to emphasize the counting of the *moves* or *jumps*—perhaps by using a large line or strip on the floor.

7 count on 5 → 12

Another way would be to use a strip and shading—preferably in different colours.

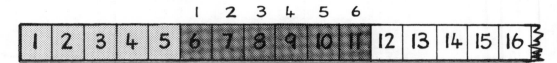

5 (shaded in red)    Count on 6 (shading in green)

There are many games and activities such as Ludo, Snakes and Ladders, dot-to-dot pictures, etc. which help in counting on or becoming familiar with the sequence of numbers.

One game which helps to connect the moves involved in counting on and addition is 'Lakes and Adders'.

*Lakes and adders*
Each player in turn rolls a die. The score tells him the number of jumps to move his token. If the player lands on 7 or 13, he has fallen into a lake and must go back to the start. The winner is the first to pass the finishing post.

The moves are recorded and, after the game, the number sentences are written at the side.

| Starting square | score | move to | Number sentence. |
|---|---|---|---|
| 0 | 5 | 5 | 0 + 5 = 5 |
| 5 | 3 | 8 | 5 + 3 = 8 |
| 8 | 5 | 13 (lake) | 8 + 5 = 13 |
| 0 | 6 | 6 | 0 + 6 = 6 |
| 6 | 5 | 11 | 6 + 5 = 11 |
| 11 | 4 | 15 | 11 + 4 = 15 |
| 15 | 6 | 21 | 15 + 6 = 21 |

Counting on activities may be used to confirm that the order in which the numbers are added does not affect the total (Worksheet N9 : 2.3). Example :

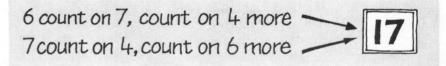

6 count on 7, count on 4 more
7 count on 4, count on 6 more  →  17

Some children may still be experiencing difficulty in counting on from any number in ones, twos, threes, etc. This is an important skill which should be practised regularly (Worksheet N9 : 2.6).

*Worksheets should not be introduced until children have had plenty of practical experience and opportunity for discussion.*

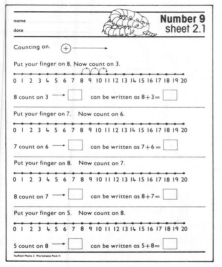

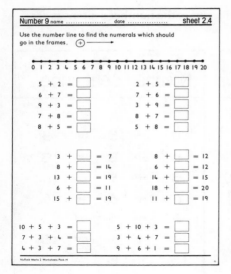

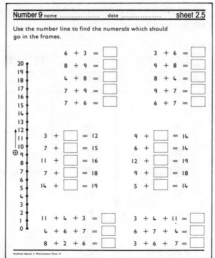

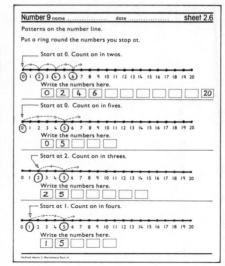

## N9: 3 Ways of Recording

The ways of recording addition used in Chapter 6 of *Nuffield Maths 1 Teachers' Handbook* can now be extended to include numbers up to 20:

$$4 + 9 = \square \qquad\qquad (4, 9) \xrightarrow{\text{add}} \square$$

$$3 + 6 + 2 = \square \qquad\qquad (3, 6, 2) \xrightarrow{+} \square$$

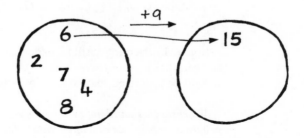

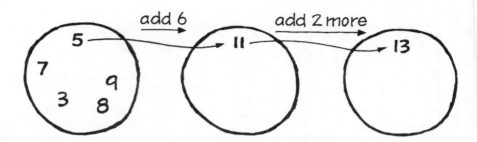

The equation or number sentence using the 'equals' sign takes recording a stage further but it should be remembered that, in making a statement in terms of abstract number, it is important to link symbols with the actions and language of addition.

| Actions | Putting sets of objects together.<br>Placing rods, bricks, etc., end to end.<br>'Jumps' on the number line/strip. |
|---|---|
| Words<br>(Spoken, then written.) | 'I had 5 and John gave me 3 more so now I have 8.'<br>'5 and 3; altogether 8'<br>'Start at 5 and count on 3. Finish on 8' |
| 'Shorthand' | $(5,3) \xrightarrow{\text{together make}} 8$<br><br>$(5,3) \xrightarrow{\text{add}} 8$<br><br>$5 \xrightarrow{\text{count on 3}} 8$ |
| Symbols | $(5,3) \xrightarrow{\quad + \quad} 8$<br><br>$\begin{array}{r} 5 \\ +3 \\ \hline 8 \\ \hline \end{array}$<br><br>$(5+3) \xrightarrow{\text{can be written as}} 8$<br>$5+3 = 8$ |

From this simplified chart it can be seen there are many activities which lead to the final equation, $5+3 = 8$. Conversely, there are several ways of interpreting the equation, that is, there could be different versions of 'the story for $5+3 = 8$'. Having gradually built up the chain:

actions → spoken words → writing → symbols,

we should also reverse the process:

symbols → what do they say? → what do they mean? → give an example.
Children need many examples to help them appreciate the links between actions, words and symbols.

*Worksheets should not be introduced until children have had plenty of practical experience and opportunity for discussion.*

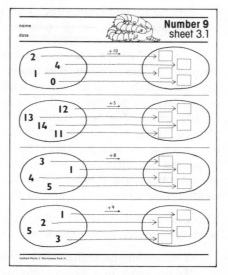

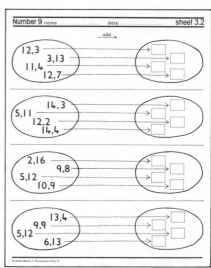

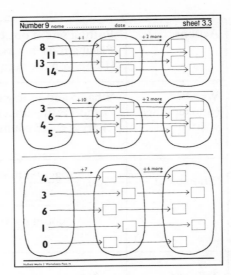

## N9:4  Estimation of numbers up to 20

Estimation was discussed at length in *Teachers' Handbook 1*, where the crux of the problem is described as follows:

> When presented with a small number of objects and asked to estimate how many there are, some children will make a wild guess; others will carry out a quick count in order to 'get it right'. The latter approach should not be looked upon as a mild form of cheating but rather as part of the build-up or valuable experience of recognizing different configurations which is closely linked to the conservation of number.
>
> We are faced with an awkward dichotomy. When calculating, we want the children to be as accurate as possible: when they are estimating, we are ready, indeed pleased, to accept any of the expressions such as: *nearly, about, roughly, almost, close to, a bit under/over, just under/over.*
>
> We have to lead children through the 'wild guess' and 'quick count' stages so that they begin to improve their attitude towards estimation and their skill at making estimates based on previous experience and knowledge. This skill will prove to be very valuable at a later stage when the numbers and measures involved are larger.

In *Teachers' Handbook 2* estimation should be encouraged throughout the number chapters as well as those on measurement. Once the children have reached the stage of dealing with numbers up to 20 (chapter N9) the worksheets can be introduced. The first worksheet, *Quick peep* extends the idea met in *Teachers' Handbook 1*, but this time as a game for two players. Again, it is important not to talk about estimates being 'wrong', but rather to see which player is better at estimating. This could be done by adding the difference column, ignoring whether the estimates are over or under the actual numbers. The better estimator is the player whose estimates have been closer and so give a lower total of differences.

This activity is developed further in *Worksheet 2*, by allowing the person holding the beads to give clues such as:

> 'I'm holding more than ten but not as many as fifteen.'
> 'In my hand there's over eight but under thirteen beads.'

This is a gentle introduction to 'betweenness', that is selecting lower and upper limits between which the exact number lies. This technique will prove very useful later on when the results of involved calculations are to be estimated in advance. (For example, the answer to $6.8 \times 3.14$ will be between $6 \times 3$ and $7 \times 4$, that is between 18 and 28. If the paper-and-pencil calculation or calculator display gives the answer as 2.1352 or 213.52, it will be obvious that a decimal point has slipped somewhere!)

*Worksheets 3* and *4* give children the chance to practise estimation skills on up to 20 objects of varying sizes or arranged in a more random fashion.

*Worksheet 5* has strong links with estimation of length. The beads cannot be counted first because they are not there to be counted! The same applies to questions 2, 3 and 4 of *Worksheet 6* because the coins cannot be counted until after they have been arranged inside the circle.

*Worksheet 7* introduces a new idea which has links with multiplication. Children have to estimate how many different ways one object from a set of three can be combined with one object from a set of two. (6 ways). Some children may be able to develop this idea further by trying to estimate how many different outfits consisting of a blouse and a skirt can be made from three blouses and three skirts. (9 outfits.)

*Worksheet 8* is investigative in nature. Commercially produced 'tockers' can be used instead of paper plates or, in the absence of both, circular discs cut from stiff card and folded in half will suffice. Once the children have experimented with one sized tocker, they must estimate how many times they can write their first names before a different sized tocker comes to rest. They may suggest other things to do and count such as 'How many towers five cubes high can I build?' or 'How many words of five letters can I write?'

Past experience has shown that, for many children, it is the attitude to estimation that needs to be changed. We must continually emphasise that estimation is a very useful skill that becomes more and more important as our work in mathematics continues.

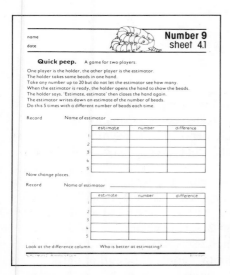

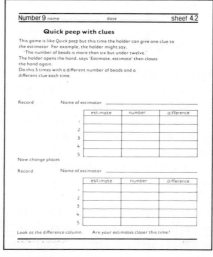

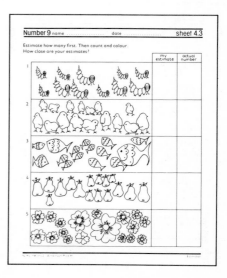

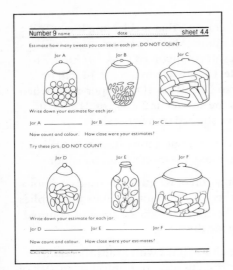

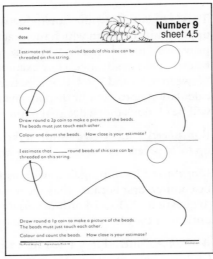

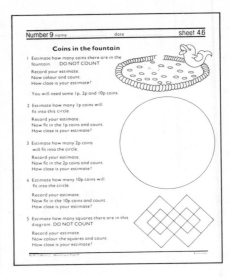

## References and resources

Frobisher, B. and Gloyn, S. *Infants Learn Mathematics*, Ward Lock 1969

Nuffield Mathematics Teaching Project, *Mathematics Begins* ①, *Computation and Structure* ②, Nuffield Guides, Chambers/Murray 1967 (See Introduction, page vii)

Pleuger, W. H. *Guide to the Use of Stern Apparatus*, E. J. Arnold 1965

Taverner, N. *Unifix Teachers' Manual*, Philip & Tacey Ltd

E. J. Arnold *Multilink Number Track, Stern Number Track*

Osmiroid, *Centicube Number Track* (*Metline*)

Philip & Tacey Ltd, *Unifix Number Track*

## Appendix

### The use of the 'equals' sign

In mathematics, the term 'equality' has a meaning more precise than is implied in such phrases as 'all men are created equal'. Equality in mathematics infers a special relationship denoted by the symbol ' = '. It is perhaps because this symbol is so familiar that it tends to be treated with contempt.

No one would take exception to the statement: 2 = 2; but it is not reasonable to say: 'These 2 apples = those 2 apples.'

In the first statement we are referring to ideas in the mind of man. There is in the physical world no such thing as 2; it is an abstract notion. In the second example we are referring to concrete objects—apples do exist, but no apple can be described as *equal* to another apple. The author of the second statement means 'the *number* of apples here (namely 2) is the same as the *number* of apples over there.'

At this stage we shall use the symbol '=' only to mean 'represents the same number as'. This is a special case of an *equivalence relation*, which is described below.

The first stage in the development of understanding number is practical experience with objects. Then comes discussion about this activity. Gradually the experiences are recorded using pictures and then words.

'I had 3 cars. John gave me 2 more so now I have 5.'

The tedium of writing is reduced by various forms of 'shorthand' recording—usually by mapping.

$$3 \text{ and } 2 \xrightarrow{\text{altogether}} 5$$

This bridges the gap between the written sentence describing what happened with the *real objects* and the final abstract statement, the equation $3 + 2 = 5$, which records the relationship between the *numbers* involved.

The introduction of '=' too early can have a disastrous effect on a child making the gradual transition from dealing with objects to coping with numbers.

### Common misuses of the '=' sign

| *What was written* | *What was meant* |
|---|---|
| 1 cm = 1 km | 1 centimetre represents 1 kilometre |
| My ribbon = 20 cm | My ribbon is about 20 cm long |
| 4 men = 52 hours | The 4 men took 52 hours |
| My weight = 34 kg | My weight is about 34 kg |
| In some words c = s | The letter 'c' sometimes sounds like the letter 's' (e.g. in cider; but not in cocoa). |

### Equivalence relations

We have discussed earlier quite a number of different relations: 'is taller than'; 'belongs to'; 'was born in'; 'has the same shape as'; 'goes to the same school as', etc.

Some relations are *symmetric*.

Example:

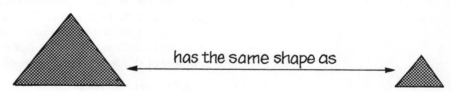

Here the two shapes could be interchanged:

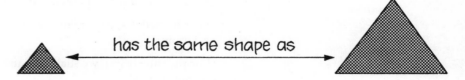

Notice the double headed arrow implying that the relation may be 'read in either direction'.

The relation 'is taller than' is not symmetric since if Ann is taller than Betty, it would not be correct to interchange Betty and Ann in the statement.

Anne    Betty    Carol

is taller than

Some relations are *transitive*.
Example:

Ann is taller than Betty.
Betty is taller than Carol. } implies Ann is taller than Carol.

The relation 'is the father of' is not transitive since if Dan is the father of Ernie and Ernie is the father of Fred, it does not follow that Dan is the father of Fred.

A relation is described as *reflexive* if each element concerned has the relationship with itself. 'Goes to the same school as' is an example of such a relation. 'John goes to the same school as John' may seem an obvious statement but not all relations are reflexive. For example, 'sits next to' is not reflexive, nor is 'has more money than'.

A relation which has all three of the properties: reflexive, and symmetric, and transitive, is called an equivalence relation.

Let us take, for example, the set of numbers with which we are concerned at present, namely (1, 2, 3, 4 . . .) and the relation 'equals' or '=', meaning 'is the same number as.'

1 Any number equals itself (reflexive property: a = a) for example, 7 = 7.
   At first sight this may seem a trivial statement because it is so obvious, but is it always obvious? Even the 'seven-ness of 7' is not obvious to infants in the early stages of their experience for we need only remember that, until the concept of conservation has developed, a set of 7 counters when spread out or moved will be counted again to check that there are still 7.

2 Symmetric property: (If a = b, then b = a)
   There again, this property in respect of numbers becomes obvious only after experience. A child putting pegs into holes sees first that he has the same number of pegs as he has holes. It may not be immediately obvious to him that he has the same number of holes as he has pegs.

3 Transitive property: (If a = b and b = c, then a = c)
   Matching with three sets of objects leads to an appreciation of the transitive property. If four children are each given a doll then the number of children is equal to the number of dolls. If each doll is then put in a cot, the number of dolls equals the number of cots. The final stage is to see that the number of children is equal to the number of cots.

   All three properties:

   1  a = a (reflexive)
   2  If a = b, then b = a (symmetric)
   3  If a = b and b = c, then a = c (transitive)

are satisfied if a, b, c are numbers, so '=' here gives an equivalence relation.

For the time being, we shall only use the sumbol '=' to denote 'is the same number as'.

Later it may be used more widely, but even then only for an equivalence relation.

# Chapter 4
# Subtraction involving numbers up to 20 (N10)

National Curriculum
Attainment Target 3: Level 2
Attainment Target 3: Level 3
Attainment Target 5: Level 3
Attainment Target 6: Level 2

## For the teacher

The three aspects of subtraction (difference, movement on a number line and physical removal) introduced in Chapter 2, are extended in this chapter to include numbers up to 20 and beyond. At this stage, formal subtraction involving 'decomposition' or 'equal additions' will not be introduced.

Some teachers prefer to use the phrase 'fewer than' as the opposite of 'more than' when dealing with countable objects; reserving 'less than' for quantities—for example, 'fewer friends' but 'less water'. It is better not to be too pedantic about this but to use whichever version is understood by the children.

## Summary of the stages

**N10**: 1 Difference by matching and counting

**N10**: 2 Subtraction by counting back

**N10**: 3 Taking away

**N10**: 4 Ways of recording.

## Vocabulary

Find the difference, difference between, less, fewer, more, match, count back, start, finish, take away, minus, how many are left?, subtract, subtraction.

## Equipment and apparatus

Rods, cubes, card strips, counters, beads, marbles, etc., number lines, squared paper.

## Working with the children

### N10 : 1    Difference by matching and counting

By referring back to the activities described in 'Finding the difference' in Chapter 2, the teacher can remind children of what is meant by 'difference' when dealing with numbers. Some practical work followed by discussion on 'pairing off' objects from two sets in order to find out 'how many more' or 'how many less'—first of all using numbers less than 10—will gradually ease the children into dealing with numbers up to 20.

The worksheets for this stage are similar in format to those used in Chapter 2 (N7). Worksheet N10 : 1.4 involves the reading off from a graph the differences between numbers of pets. A graph made by a group of children about their own pets, favourite television programmes, etc. would have much more relevance for the children.

The various forms of language and symbols for recording are used in the worksheets:

The difference between 11 and 6 is □

11 > 6 by □

11 − 6 = □

There are □ more circles than rectangles.

There are □ fewer rabbits than guinea pigs.

*Worksheets should not be introduced until children have had plenty of practical experience and opportunity for discussion.*

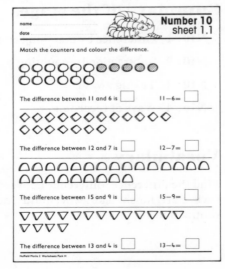

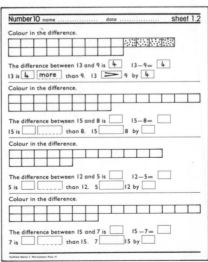

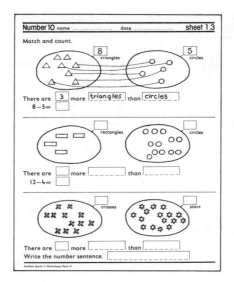

## N10: 2 Subtraction by counting back

The children may need to be reminded that subtraction by counting back involves moving towards the smaller numbers and that it is the number of *jumps* which they count—they should not tap the starting point.

A number line and strips of card cut to precise lengths may be used with a group of children to show another way of subtracting—this time without having to count jumps.

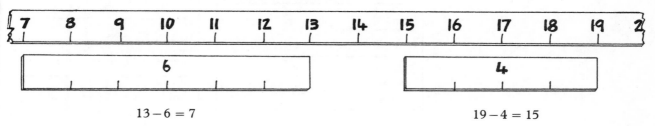

$$13 - 6 = 7 \qquad\qquad 19 - 4 = 15$$

Start at 19. Count back in fours.

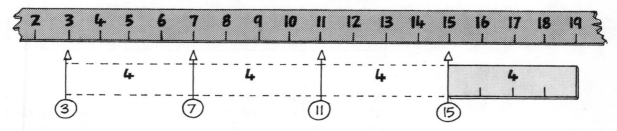

The repeated subtraction of the same number is good preparation for the later development of division.

Alternatively, number tracks produced by Stern, Unifix, Multilink, Centicubes, etc. can be used for a similar activity.

Both vertical and horizontal number lines are used in the worksheets.

The symbols

remind children of the direction of movement involved.

45

Some of the counting back questions are in the form

$16 - \square = 9$

'If I start at 16, how many do I count back to reach 9?'

*Worksheets should not be introduced until children have had plenty of practical experience and opportunity for discussion.*

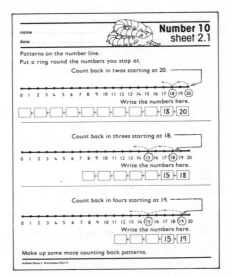

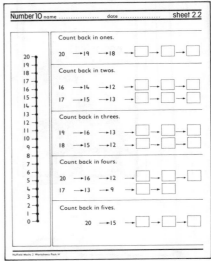

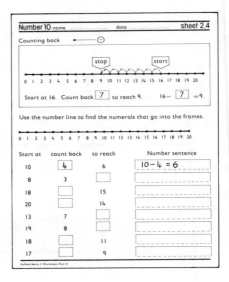

### N10: 3 Taking away

The physical basis of 'take away' described in Chapter 2 should be presented to the children again using real objects and perhaps the 'John and Peter' board.

The children should be encouraged to make up their own situations using as many different expressions as possible to imply 'take away' (lost, gave away, sold, dropped off, ate, etc.), then to demonstrate or 'set out' the story using objects, then to record what has happened. The reverse process ('Tell me a story for $10 - 6 = 4$') is also important. Gradually the number of objects involved can be increased up to 20.

The worksheets for this stage include story pictures, crossing through to represent taking away and, finally, word problems which may require help from the teacher for children with reading difficulties. However, by placing the 'word version' as close as possible to the 'symbol version', it is hoped the help required will be kept to a minimum. Even so, some children may need to use a picture or diagram to bridge the gap between words and symbols.

*Worksheets should not be introduced until children have had plenty of practical experience and opportunity for discussion.*

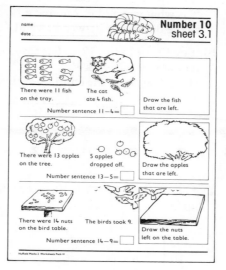

**Sheet 3.1 (Number 10)**

There were 11 fish on the tray. The cat ate 4 fish. Draw the fish that are left.
Number sentence 11−4=

There were 13 apples on the tree. 5 apples dropped off. Draw the apples that are left.
Number sentence 13−5=

There were 14 nuts on the bird table. The birds took 9. Draw the nuts left on the table.
Number sentence 14−9=

**Sheet 3.2 (Number 10)**

Here are 16 circles. Take away 7 circles. There are 9 left.
16−7= 9

Here are 15 squares. Take away 8 squares. There are □ left.
15−8=

Here are 17 triangles. Take away 5 triangles. There are □ left.
17−5=

Here are 19 oblongs. Take away 15 oblongs. There are □ left.
19−15=

**Sheet 3.3 (Number 10)**

11−9=  16−13=  12−7=
13−5=  18−14=  14−11=
19−10=  15−8=  20−12=
13−13=  14−10=  15−0=

**Sheet 3.4 (Number 10)**

There were 9 birds on a fence. 9
5 birds flew away. −5
How many are left? ___

John had 11 sweets. 11
He eats 4. −4
How many are left? ___

There were 14 candles lit. □
9 are blown out.
How many are still lit? ___

Bill had 17 counters. □
He lost 5. How many has he now? ___

14 sailor boys sailing on the sea,
11 jumped overboard,
then there were ... □

20 ladies, waiting for the Queen,
6 went home again,
and left ... □

There were 16 apples on a tree. Mary picked some and left 11. How many did she pick?
16− □ =11.

A baker started with 20 cakes. He sold some and had 13 left. How many did he sell?
20− □ =13

Make up your own 'take away' stories or rhymes.

## N10 : 4 Ways of recording

The worksheets for this section provide practice in subtraction set out in a variety of ways—mapping, vertical subtraction, 'more than' or 'less than' forms and 'missing number' problems. The important link between addition and subtraction, which is used constantly when 'giving change', is emphasized by problems set in blocks :

12 − 4 = □        4 + □ = 12

12 − 8 = □        8 + □ = 12

A valuable and revealing insight into how subtraction is tackled can often be gained by asking the child to explain how he arrived at his answer. Here are a few examples:

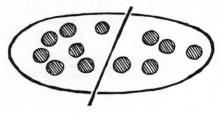

a) Some children are able to use number bonds with which they are already familiar:

'I know $12 - 7 = 5$ because $7 + 5 = 12$'.
'5 is what you add to 7 to make 12,
so the difference between 12 and 7 is 5'.

b) 'For $17 - 9$ I said, $17 - 10$ is easy—it's 7. $17 - 9$ means I must not go so far back, so $17 - 9$ is 8'.
Here, it appears the child was thinking on the number line.

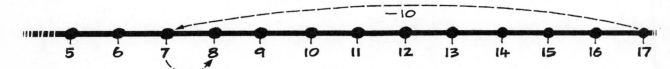

c) $17 - 9$. 'Well, $17 - 7$ is 10, so $17 - 9$ is 8 because 2 more have to come off'.

$$\left.\begin{array}{r} 17 \\ -\ 7 \\ \hline 10 \\ -\ 2 \\ \hline 8 \end{array}\right\} -9$$

d) $14 - 8$. '14 is 10 and 4. If I crossed out 8 in the 10 I'd have 2. So I've got 2 and 4 which is 6.'

```
0 0
∅ ∅
∅ ∅  0 0
∅ ∅  0 0
∅ ∅
```
$(10 - 8) + 4$

If 'subtraction squares' or 'subtraction oblongs' are used, care must be taken to 'read' the question in the correct direction because subtraction is not commutative—i.e. $7 - 5$ does not give the same result as $5 - 7$.

Each of the numbers on the top row should be greater than or at least equal to any number in the left-hand column in order to avoid negative answers.

This must be read from the top row:

From 13 subtract 5,
$13 - 5 = 8$

From

| − | 11 | 12 | 13 | 14 | 15 |
|---|---|---|---|---|---|
| 3 |  |  |  |  |  |
| 4 |  |  |  |  |  |
| 5 |  |  | 8 |  |  |
| 6 |  |  |  |  |  |
| 7 |  |  |  |  |  |

Subtract

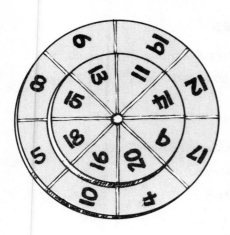

'Moving Targets' similar to those suggested in Chapter 3, can also be used for subtraction practice—provided each of the numbers on the inner circle is greater than any on the outer circle.

$19 - 11 =$

$14 - 12 =$

$17 - 9 =$

etc.

When the inner circle is moved round another eight subtraction problems appear, and so on.

Some children may be able to use a pattern approach for numbers over 20:

$7 - 3 = 4 \qquad 17 - 3 = 14 \qquad 27 - 3 = 24$ etc.

*Worksheets should not be introduced until children have had plenty of practical experience and opportunity for discussion.*

# References and resources

Pleuger, W. H. *Guide to the Use of Stern Apparatus*, E. J. Arnold 1965

Shuard, H. and Williams, E. M. *Primary Mathematics Today*, Longman Group UK Ltd 1976

Taverner, N. *Unifix Teachers' Manual*, Philip & Tacey Ltd

E. J. Arnold *Multilink Number Track, Stern Number Track*

Osmiroid, *Centicube Number Track (Metline)*

Philip & Tacey Ltd, *Unifix Number Track*

# Chapter 5
# Introducing multiplication (N11)

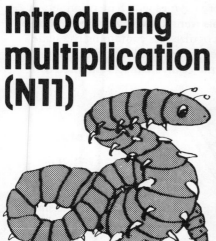

National Curriculum
Attainment Target 3: Level 3
Attainment Target 5: Level 3
Attainment Target 12: Level 2

## For the teacher

Chapter 2 of *Nuffield Maths 1 Teacher's Handbook* introduced the idea of equivalent sets, that is sets having the same number of members. Gradually, children become more aware of examples of equivalent sets all around them—two eyes, two legs, three wheels on tricycles, four children at each table, etc. In this chapter the idea of counting in twos, threes, fours, etc., is used as a starting point in the development of multiplication, limiting the products obtained to not more than 30.

## Summary of the stages

**N11**: 1    Recognizing and counting equivalent sets

**N11**: 2    Multiplication as repeated addition

**N11**: 3    Arrays and the commutative law

**N11**: 4    Activities and games for 'table facts' up to 30

## Vocabulary

Twos, threes, fours, etc., sets of, lots of, subsets, multiply, multiplied by, times, product, array, rows, columns.

## Equipment and apparatus

Counting materials such as cubes, counters, beads, bottle-tops, etc., pegs and pegboards, dice, squared paper, rods, number lines, strips of card.

# Working with the children

### N11 : 1  Recognizing and counting equivalent sets

There are many songs, games and nursery rhymes which mention sets of 2, 3, 4—Three Little Kittens', 'The animals went in two by two', etc. These can be used to establish that children recognize sets containing the same number of members. Sorting trays and counters, shells or other counting materials can then be used, first to sort into equivalent sets and then to count the number of sets.

Two shells in each box.

There are 4 sets of 2.

Building towers of cubes and threading beads on a string provide similar experiences:

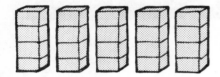

5 sets of 4

4 sets of 3

Stories also give opportunities for counting the number of equivalent sets. For example, 'How many sets of 2 legs, and how many sets of 4 legs are there in "The Gingerbread Man"?'

At this stage it is important to ensure that

a) the children can recognize equivalent sets, and

b) they are able to count the number of *sets*, rather than the number of objects

*Worksheets should not be introduced until children have had plenty of practical experience and opportunity for discussion.*

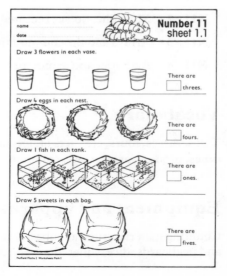

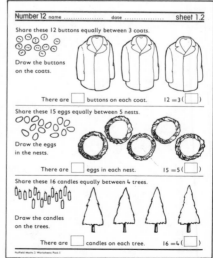

**N11 : 2  Multiplication as repeated addition.**

Having sorted into equivalent sets, the children should be encouraged to answer the questions, 'How many is that altogether?' by counting in twos, three, fours, etc. This should be started as a practical activity with discussion stimulated by the teacher leading gradually to pictorial and numerical recording.

1 set of 2 ⟶ 2

2 sets of 2    2 + 2 ⟶ 4

3 sets of 2    2 + 2 + 2 ⟶ 6

1 chair ⟶ 4 legs

2 chairs    4 + 4 ⟶ 8 legs

3 chairs    4 + 4 + 4 ⟶ 12 legs

4 chairs    4 + 4 + 4 + 4 ⟶ 16 legs

| Number of chairs | 0 | 1 | 2 | 3 | 4 | 5 | 6 | 7 |
|---|---|---|---|---|---|---|---|---|
| Number of legs | 0 | 4 | 8 | 12 | 16 | 20 | 24 | 28 |

The build-up of 'equal sized steps' is very important and should be emphasized by recording in the form of a block graph.

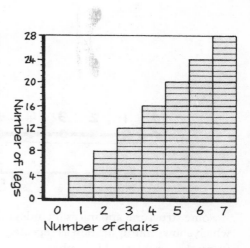

Two other examples are very important:

1 set of 1 ⟶ 1

2 sets of 1    1 + 1 ⟶ 2

3 sets of 1    1 + 1 + 1 ⟶ 3 etc.

This eventually leads to the idea, 'Multiplying a number by 1 does not change it.'

53

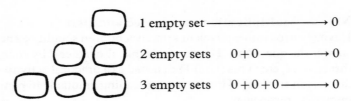

1 empty set ⎯⎯⎯⎯⎯⎯⎯⎯→ 0

2 empty sets  $0 + 0$ ⎯⎯⎯⎯⎯⎯→ 0

3 empty sets  $0 + 0 + 0$ ⎯⎯⎯⎯→ 0

This seemingly trivial example will later become 'the nought-times table'—a common area for mistakes in calculation—and lead to the idea, 'Any number multiplied by 0 is 0.'

Another valuable activity is 'Hops on a number line.' This is best done with a group of children using a large number line—perhaps marked out on the floor. By starting a zero the 'table of twos' or the 'table of threes' etc. can be built up by recording the 'landings'.

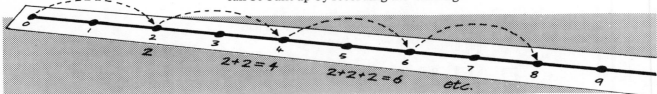

Alternatively, a cardboard number line and smaller pieces of lengths 2 units, 3 units, 4 units can be used.

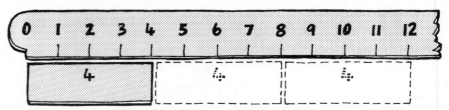

Structural apparatus and a number line made to match the unit-size of the material can be used in a similar manner.

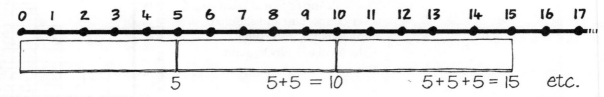

Some structural apparatus includes number track which shows multiplication as repeated addition using rods or interlocking cubes:

Unifix supply multiplication markers—plastic dividers which fit between Unifix cubes when assembled as a bar:

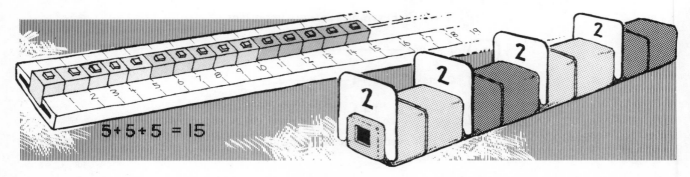

This type of activity should be continued but recording modified by using the 'shorthand' version:

$3+3+3+3$ becomes '4 sets of 3' which can be written as 4 (3).

The numeral inside the brackets denotes the number of members in each set; the numeral in front of the brackets tells how many sets there are.

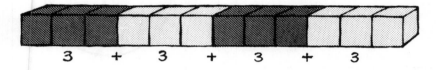

3 + 3 + 3 + 3

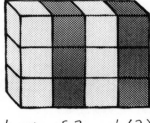

4 sets of 3    4(3)

Initially, both forms of recording should be used.

There are 3 flowers.

Each flower has 5 petals.

How many petals altogether?

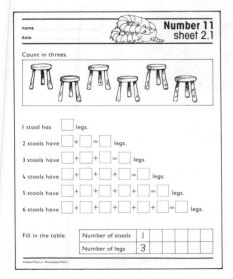

$5 + 5 + 5$ ⎯⎯→ ☐

$3(5)$ ⎯⎯⎯⎯⎯→ ☐

Even when children appear confident in using the form 3(5), it is advisable, from time to time, to ask them to explain what 3(5) means and to write out the full version, $5 + 5 + 5$.

*Worksheets should not be introduced until children have had plenty of practical experience and opportunity for discussion.*

---

name .............
date .............

**Number 11**
sheet 2.1

Count in threes.

1 stool has ☐ legs.

2 stools have ☐ + ☐ = ☐ legs.

3 stools have ☐ + ☐ + ☐ = ☐ legs.

4 stools have ☐ + ☐ + ☐ + ☐ = ☐ legs.

5 stools have ☐ + ☐ + ☐ + ☐ + ☐ = ☐ legs.

6 stools have ☐ + ☐ + ☐ + ☐ + ☐ + ☐ = ☐ legs.

Fill in the table.

| Number of stools | 1 | | | | | |
|---|---|---|---|---|---|---|
| Number of legs | 3 | | | | | |

Nuffield Maths 2 Worksheets Pack 1

---

Number 11 name .............. date ..............

sheet 2.2

Count in fives.

| 1 foot | Number of toes | Table of fives |
|---|---|---|
| | | 1 (5) = ☐ |
| 2 feet | ☐ + ☐ = ☐ | 2 (5) = ☐ |
| 3 feet | ☐ + ☐ + ☐ = ☐ | 3 (5) = ☐ |
| 4 feet | ☐ + ☐ + ☐ + ☐ = ☐ | 4 (5) = ☐ |
| 5 feet | ☐ + ☐ + ☐ + ☐ + ☐ = ☐ | 5 (5) = ☐ |
| 6 feet | ☐ + ☐ + ☐ + ☐ + ☐ + ☐ = ☐ | 6 (5) = ☐ |

Put a ring round the table of fives.

| 1 | 2 | 3 | 4 | ⑤ | 6 | 7 | 8 | 9 | 10 |
|---|---|---|---|---|---|---|---|---|---|
| 11 | 12 | 13 | 14 | 15 | 16 | 17 | 18 | 19 | 20 |
| 21 | 22 | 23 | 24 | 25 | 26 | 27 | 28 | 29 | 30 |

Nuffield Maths 2 Worksheets Pack 1

---

name .............
date .............

**Number 11**
sheet 2.3

Count in fours.

1 car has ☐ wheels.     1 (4) = ☐

2 cars have ☐ wheels.    2 (4) = ☐

3 cars have ☐ wheels.    3 (4) = ☐

4 cars have ☐ wheels.    4 (4) = ☐

5 cars have ☐ wheels.    5 (4) = ☐

6 cars have ☐ wheels.    6 (4) = ☐

Shade in the squares for the table of fours.

1 car
2 cars
3 cars
4 cars
5 cars
6 cars

Nuffield Maths 2 Worksheets Pack 1

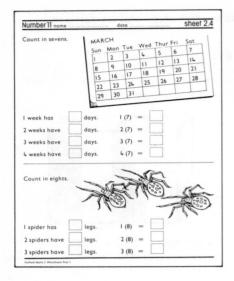

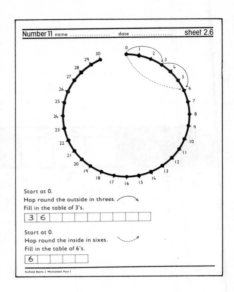

### N11: 3 Arrays and the commutative law

Children will be familiar with objects arranged in rectangular patterns of arrays. Egg boxes, bars of chocolate, milk crates, etc. all provide opportunities for counting in rows or columns. The children may need to be told or reminded that we usually call lines across, 'rows' and lines up and down 'columns'. Examples of rows and columns are given in the Project's Bronto Book, 'Left, right'.

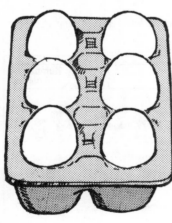

3 rows of 2
2 columns of 3

$2+2+2=6$
$3+3 \quad =6$
$3(2) \quad =6$
$2(3) \quad =6$

4 rows of 2
2 columns of 4

$2+2+2+2 \quad =8$
$4+4 \quad =8$
$4(2) \quad =8$
$2(4) \quad =8$

The fact that 3(2) and 2(3) are both ways of writing 6 demonstrates that multiplication is commutative. This is important because, later on, it reduces the number of 'table facts' to be learned by half.

In the real world of measurement 3(2) and 2(3) or $3 \times 2$ and $2 \times 3$ are not always the same. Two 3-metre lengths of curtain material are not the same as three 2-metre lengths.

Some people may argue that $5 \times 2$ should be interpreted as, 'Five multiplied by two' or 'A set of five objects twice'. To insist upon this interpretation is likely to confuse children if, at the same time, we want them to appreciate the commutative property of multiplication. Ideally, children should see 10, for example, as either 2 subsets of 5 or as 5 subsets of 2.

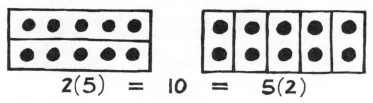

$$2(5) \quad = \quad 10 \quad = \quad 5(2)$$

They should also see that 10 is the *product* obtained for 5 multiplied by 2 or from 2 multiplied by 5.

$5 \times 2 = 2 \times 5 = 10$

Using rods to illustrate the same example,

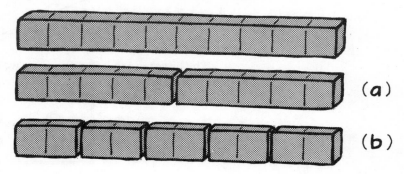

a) can be described as:
   either '2 rods of 5 units each'
   or      The 5-rod used twice'

b) can be described as:
   either '5 rods of 2 units each'
   or      'The 2-rod used 5 times'

The word 'times' may arise when describing activities involving 'loads'. For example: Each time the truck brings 4 cubes:

| | |
|---|---|
| The first time it brings | 4 cubes, |
| The second time it brings | 4 cubes, |
| The third time it brings | 4 cubes, |
| Altogether it brings | 12 cubes |

How many times did the truck bring a load?
   Three times.
How many cubes in each load?
   Four cubes.
How many cubes altogether?
   Twelve.
Three times four is twelve.

Gradually, the symbol × —'multiplied by' can be introduced, e.g. 3 × 4 and read 'Three multiplied by four' or 'Three times four'. However, it is preferable if the children do *not* use 'times' as a verb as in, 'I timesed it by four.'

'*Partnering*' Another way of looking at multiplication is by 'partnering', where each member of the first set is in turn partnered with each member of the second set. For example, if there are two members of a set of riders and three members of a set of horses and each rider rides on each horse, how many different pairs could there be?

We could record by using a line to show each pairing. The number of lines gives the number of different pairs.

*Set of riders*
(2 members)

*Set of horses*
(3 members)

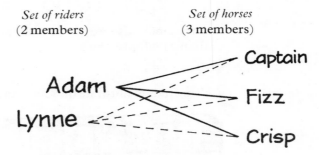

The lines tend to be confused, so we could record by using a table in the form of an array:

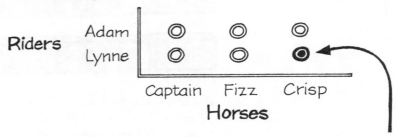

Each counter represents a different pair. For example, this counter represents the pair (Lynne, Crisp).

This is a much more organized way of recording all the members of the set of pairs than just writing them down and possibly omitting some. Once the array has been obtained, the number of pairs can be counted either in rows or columns, to give 6 as the product of 2 and 3.

*Worksheets should not be introduced until children have had plenty of practical experience and opportunity for discussion.*

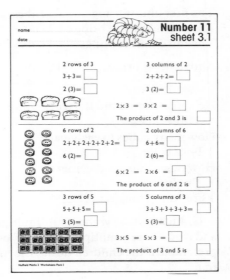

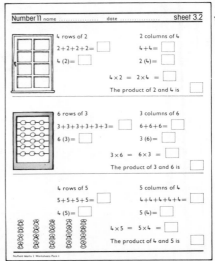

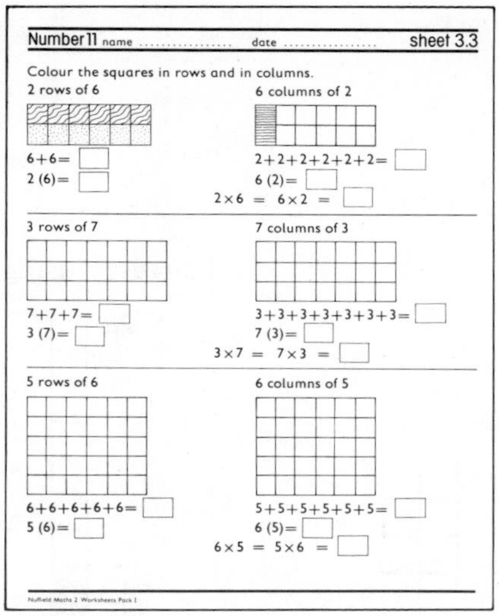

Sheet 3.3:

Number 11 name .............. date .............. sheet 3.3

Colour the squares in rows and in columns.

2 rows of 6 | 6 columns of 2

6+6= ☐
2 (6) = ☐

2+2+2+2+2+2= ☐
6 (2) = ☐
2×6 = 6×2 = ☐

3 rows of 7 | 7 columns of 3

7+7+7= ☐
3 (7) = ☐

3+3+3+3+3+3+3= ☐
7 (3) = ☐
3×7 = 7×3 = ☐

5 rows of 6 | 6 columns of 5

6+6+6+6+6= ☐
5 (6) = ☐

5+5+5+5+5+5= ☐
6 (5) = ☐
6×5 = 5×6 = ☐

Nuffield Maths 2 Worksheets Pack 1

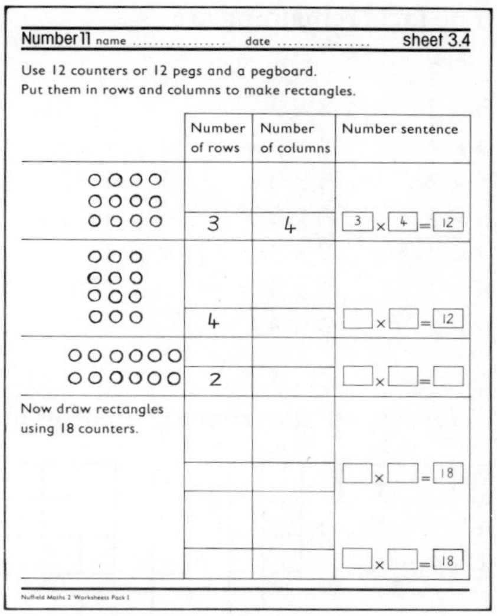

Sheet 3.4:

Number 11 name .............. date .............. sheet 3.4

Use 12 counters or 12 pegs and a pegboard.
Put them in rows and columns to make rectangles.

| | Number of rows | Number of columns | Number sentence |
|---|---|---|---|
| oooo oooo oooo | 3 | 4 | 3 × 4 = 12 |
| ooo ooo ooo ooo | 4 | | ☐ × ☐ = 12 |
| oooooo oooooo | 2 | | ☐ × ☐ = ☐ |
| Now draw rectangles using 18 counters. | | | |
| | | | ☐ × ☐ = 18 |
| | | | ☐ × ☐ = 18 |

Nuffield Maths 2 Worksheets Pack 1

## N11 : 4 Activities and games for 'table facts' up to 30

It is frustrating for a child to realize that he requires multiplication in order to solve a problem but then have to stop and ponder about $3 \times 7$. On the other hand, it must be just as frustrating to have learned table facts by rote and then not be sure how to apply them.

It need not be a question of choice between:

'I can't remember the facts I need'
and, 'I know the facts but can't use them.'

The gathering and remembering of multiplication facts should be a gradual process based on a variety of activities carefully planned to promote understanding, bolster confidence and facilitate memorization.

The first three sections of this chapter concentrated on the promotion of understanding; this section is devoted to suggestions for bolstering confidence and providing motivation to make 'learning tables' easier.

At this stage we have limited the products to not more than 30, although some children may wish and be able to continue patterns beyond 30. The number of facts to be learned is further reduced if children are reminded that:

1  Multiplying by 1 leaves a number unchanged ($9 \times 1 = 9$).
2  Any number multiplied by 0 is 0 ($8 \times 0 = 0$).
3  Multiplication works backwards and forwards ($3 \times 7 = 7 \times 3$) (Commutative Law).
4  Multiplying by 10 moves the units figure into the tens position ($3 \times 10 = 30$).

The facts remaining are:

$2 \times 2$

$3 \times 2$     $3 \times 3$

$4 \times 2$     $4 \times 3$     $4 \times 4$

$5 \times 2$     $5 \times 3$     $5 \times 4$     $5 \times 5$

$6 \times 2$     $6 \times 3$     $6 \times 4$     $6 \times 5$

$7 \times 2$     $7 \times 3$     $7 \times 4$

$8 \times 2$     $8 \times 3$

$9 \times 2$     $9 \times 3$

*Colouring rectangles* made up of small squares.

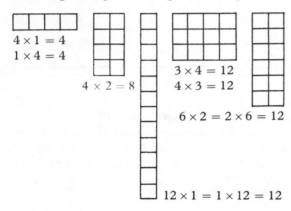

$4 \times 1 = 4$
$1 \times 4 = 4$

$4 \times 2 = 8$

$3 \times 4 = 12$
$4 \times 3 = 12$

$6 \times 2 = 2 \times 6 = 12$

$12 \times 1 = 1 \times 12 = 12$

'Multiplication patterns'
using first 3 rows of a 100 square.

Pattern of 3's.     Each table has its
own pattern.

'Staircases' using rods or squared paper.

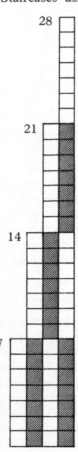

*Dominoes* See Appendix I for a set of dominoes using products. These should be copied on to cards measuring about 10 cm by 5 cm. This game can be played by up to 4 players starting with 4 dominoes each. It is similar to the usual game of dominoes—when a player 'cannot go' he takes an extra domino from those left face down in the middle of the table. The winner is the first player to use all his dominoes.

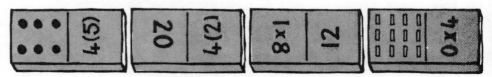

The set of dominoes may also be used by a single player for 'domino patience'.

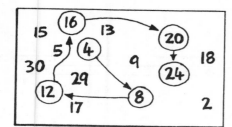

'*Join the family*'
The family of 4
The members of the family of 4 are ringed and joined in order.

It is a good exercise for children to make up these for their friends.

*Games using two standard dice*
(N.B. These games include $6 \times 6 = 36$.)

Multiplication only
Each player in turn rolls two dice, works out the product of the numbers obtained and covers the corresponding square on his card with a counter.
For example,

If he rolls [dice], $3 \times 4 = 12$, so he covers 12.

The player who covers his card first wins.

Product, difference and sum
This time the player may cover the product difference and sum of the two numbers obtained on the dice.
For example,

If he rolls [dice], $5 \times 3 = 15$, $5 - 3 = 2$ and $5 + 3 = 8$, so he covers 15, 2 and 8.

The object of this game is to try to get children to think of multiplication as a way of combining two numbers as well as by adding them or finding their difference.

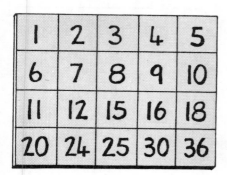

*The multiplication square*  A square can be built up to show the commutative property for multiplication in a similar way to the addition square used in earlier chapters. The products form a symmetrical pattern on either side of the dotted diagonal. For example, $5 \times 2 = 10$ and $2 \times 5 = 10$.

| × | 0 | 1 | 2 | 3 | 4 | 5 | 6 |
|---|---|---|---|---|---|---|---|
| 0 | 0 | 0 | 0 | 0 | 0 | 0 | 0 |
| 1 | 0 | 1 | 2 | 3 | 4 | 5 | 6 |
| 2 | 0 | 2 | 4 | 6 | 8 | 10 | 12 |
| 3 | 0 | 3 | 6 | 9 |   |   |   |
| 4 | 0 | 4 | 8 |   | 16 |   |   |
| 5 | 0 | 5 | 10 |   |   |   |   |
| 6 | 0 | 6 | 12 |   |   |   |   |

*Worksheets should not be introduced until children have had plenty of practical experience and opportunity for discussion.*

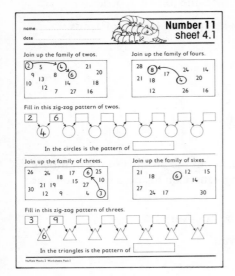

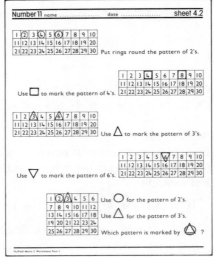

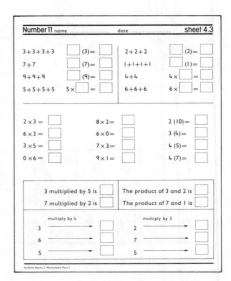

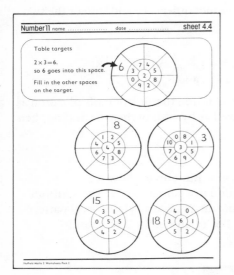

# References and resources

Burke, P. *Left, right*, Bronto Books Set B, Nuffield Maths 5–11, Longman Group UK Ltd 1979

Nuffield Mathematics Teaching Project, *Computation and Structure* ③, Nuffield Guide, Chambers/Murray 1967 (See Introduction, page vii)

Pleuger, W. H. *Guide to the Use of Stern Apparatus*, E. J. Arnold 1965

Shuard, H. and Williams, E. M. *Primary Mathematics Today*, Longman Group UK Ltd 1976

Taverner, N. *Unifix Teachers' Manual*, Philip & Tacey Ltd

E. J. Arnold *Multilink Number Track, Multilink 100 Pegboard, Stern Number Track*

Osmiroid, *Centicube Number Track (Metline)*

Philip & Tacey, Ltd, *Unifix 100 Board, Unifix Multiplication/Division Markers, Window Markers and Number Tablets*

# Appendix

| | | | | | |
|---|---|---|---|---|---|
| / 0 × 4 | 1 × 8 / 12 | 10 / 5 × 6 | 4 × 7 / 4 | 8 / 6(4) | 4 (5) / |
| 4 × 4 / 5 | 7 / 10 × 3 | 3 × 9 / 0 | 0 / 2 × 8 | 1 × 5 / 16 | 14 / 7 × 1 |
| 2 (9) / 21 | 15 / 7 × 2 | 4 (2) / 20 | / 2 × 5 | 9 × 2 / | 2 × 3 / |
| 18 / 2 × 2 | 8 × 3 / 30 | 25 / 3(7) | 28 / 3 × 6 | 30 / 5(3) | 3 × 4 / 27 |
| / 3 × 3 | 2 × 10 / 24 | 5 × 5 / | 3 × 0 / | | |

# Chapter 6
# Introducing division (N12)

## For the teacher

When introducing division to young children it is important that they are given plenty of experience of *two* aspects—*sharing* and *repeated subtraction*. In the early stages much depends upon the *rearrangement* of the members of a set. It is essential that this is done in a practical way by actually moving objects, counters, etc. into different groupings. These activities need to be carefully structured with discussion stimulated by the teacher.

Encouraging the correct use of language is particularly important because in the past some inaccurate and positively misleading expressions have been used to describe division. For example, such expressions as 'How many 5's in 15?' (This could receive the answer, 'One'), '5's into 15' (This probably led some children to call division problems 'gozinters') and 'Share 15 by 5' are all more likely to confuse than to help understanding. More acceptable versions are included in the following comparison of the two aspects

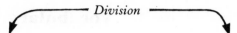

| Sharing | Repeated subtraction |
|---|---|
| Sometimes called 'partition' or the 'partitive aspect'. | Sometimes called 'quotition', 'grouping' or the 'measuring aspect'. |

| | |
|---|---|
| The number of subsets or partitions is known; the problem asks how many should go into each sub-set. | The number required in each sub-set is known; the problem asks how many subsets there will be. |
| *Example*<br>Share 8 sweets equally between 2 children. | *Example*<br>If I have 8 sweets and give 2 to each child, how many children receive sweets? |

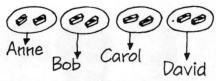

No more left for Ed, Fay, etc.

| | |
|---|---|
| Each child receives 4 sweets. This is usually done by children *sharing* the sweets out on a 'one for you, one for me' basis. | 4 *children* receive sweets. This is done by *repeatedly subtracting* 2 sweets as each child 'comes to the head of the queue'.<br>'Sharing' would not be appropriate here as we do not know how many 'shareholders' there are! |
| We know how many 'customers'. What is the share for each? | We know what the quota or ration is. How many 'customers' can we serve? |
| $2 (\square) = 8$<br>'2 sets of how many make 8?' | $\square (2) = 8$<br>'How many sets of 2 make 8?' |
| 'Share 8 sweets between 2 children' rather than '8 shared by 2'. | |

When dealing with objects or with structural apparatus, these two aspects of division are *quite different* to the child. Only after a lot of practical experience will he begin to see that there is a connection between the two aspects.

## Summary of the stages

**N12**: 1   The sharing aspect of division

**N12**: 2   The repeated subtraction aspect of division

**N12**: 3   Division as the inverse of multiplication

**N12**: 4   Remainders

## Vocabulary

Share, equally, between, subtract, divide, divided by, half, quarter, arrange into equal subsets, row, column, remainder.

## Equipment and apparatus

Collections of objects (beads, buttons, shells, counters, etc.), sorting trays, structural apparatus, number lines.

## Working with the children

### N12: 1   The sharing aspect of division

Given a bag of sweets, a young child will find a way to share it between himself and two friends. He matches one sweet to each child, then another, then another and so on until the bag of sweets is empty.

In this sort of situation the language used would be along the lines of:

one sweet each...

then another,

then another,

and so on....

'Share these sweets equally between 3 children.'
'How many sweets does each child get?'
'Arrange these counters into 4 equal subsets.'
'How many counters in each subset?'

It is important that the child is able to pick out the number of shares or subsets and the number of objects in each subset. Initially, he is probably not particularly interested in the size of the share, i.e. how many sweets they each have. It is enough to know that they each have a fair share.

Frequently the child may discover that he has one or two sweets left over. This is the first experience of what is later conventionally known as a remainder. In the early stages it is advisable to concentrate on situations which are structured so that there are no remainders.

When dealing with *continuous* materials (such as clay, ribbon or water), rather than countable or *discrete* objects, children may use balancing, folding or visual judgement:

Finding *half* of a piece of clay by balancing.

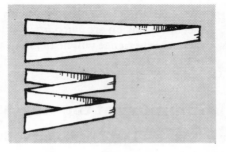

Finding *half* and then a *quarter* of a length of ribbon by folding.

Sharing water equally between three beakers by visual judgement.

Here it is essential to stress the *equality* of the halves or of the quarters. Many children interpret 'cutting in half' as just cutting into two parts rather than two *equal* parts.

*Worksheets should not be introduced until children have had plenty of practical experience and opportunity for discussion.*

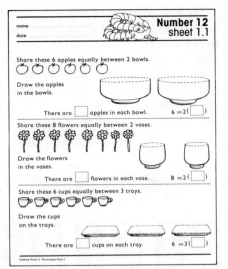

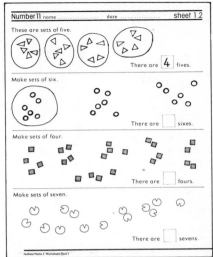

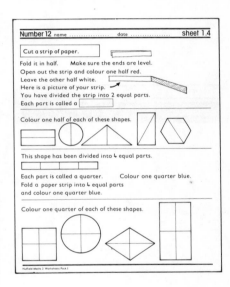

## N12: 2   The repeated subtraction aspect of division

To give experience of repeated subtraction the question would have to be: 'How many children can each have three sweets from this packet?'

Three are removed and given to the first child, then another three for the second child and so on. When all the sweets have been removed or when there are not enough left in the packet to give out another three, the number of children with three sweets each has to be counted.

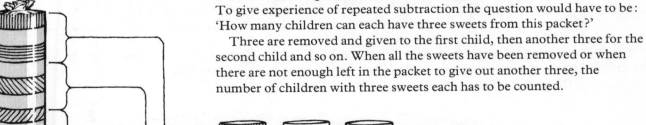

for Bill

for Mary

for Alison

for Peter

There are no sweets left for Sue, John, Kate, etc.★

4 children can be given 3 sweets each.

*It is important to point out that, because all the sweets have been given out, these children will not receive any. The 'giving out in threes' was done in order to find out how many children would be lucky. The children who received sweets have to be counted up to answer the question. The object of the exercise is defeated if the teacher allows only 4 children to be considered in the first place. This point arises in some of the problems on the worksheets.

For example:

12 stars.       Put 4 stars on a card.

3 cards have stars on them.
Only the cards which are used are counted.

The word 'measuring' becomes more appropriate for this aspect of division when structural apparatus is used.

How many 2-rods do you need to make a 10-rod? □ (2) = 10

Here, the 2-rod is used as a 'measure' in the same way that a hand span may be used to measure the length of a table.

The range of numbers may be extended by making cardboard strips up to 20 units in length.

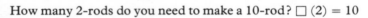

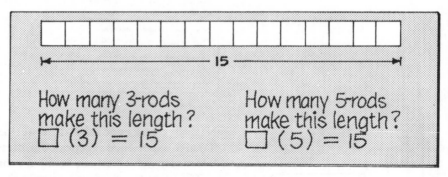

In the case of interlocking cubes such as Centicubes, Multilink, Unifix, etc. colour may be used to show, for example, the number of sets of 2 in 8:

Unifix Multiplication/Division Markers show 8 divided into 4 sets of 2:

The repeated subtraction aspect of division may also be illustrated by 'hops back on the number line'. This activity is similar to that described in the Multiplication section of Chapter 5—but this time the movement is towards zero, starting at the number to be divided.

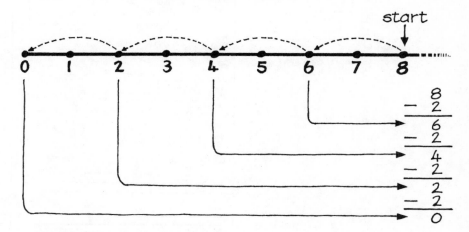

Starting at eight and hopping in twos, it takes four hops to reach zero.

$$8 = \boxed{4}\,(2)$$

Grouping games using the children, also give valuable experience. The teacher calls out, 'Join hands in fours' and the number of sets of four counted.

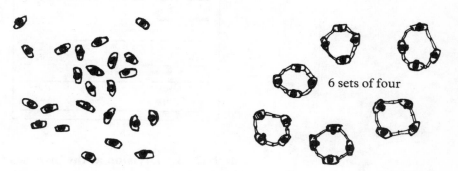

6 sets of four

The question asked here is, 'How many sets of 4 can we make from 24? or □ (4) = 24.

Unless the teacher has arranged for a suitable number of children to take part in advance, remainders are likely to arise. This may provide a good opportunity for introducing the idea of remainders as 'those remaining' after the groups have been formed. (The topic of remainders is dealt with more fully in section N12: 4.)

In the case of continuous materials, the repeated subtraction aspect of division involves finding the number of times a fixed amount may be removed by cutting, pouring, etc. How many spoonfuls of water are there in a cup? How many cups of tea can be poured from that full tea-pot? How many skipping ropes, each 2 metres long, can be cut from 14 metres of rope? Kitchen measures and jugs marked in cups, tablespoons, etc. are very useful here.

*Worksheets should not be introduced until children have had plenty of practical experience and opportunity for discussion.*

**Number 12**
sheet 2.1

name
date

6 leaves.  Put 2 leaves on a twig.

[ 3 ] twigs have leaves on them.  6 = [ 3 ] (2)

15 beads.  Put 3 beads on a string.

[ ] strings have beads on them.  15 = [ ] (3)

12 stars.  Put 4 stars on a card.

[ ] cards have stars on them.  12 = [ ] (4)

18 candles.  Put 6 on a cake.

[ ] cakes have candles on them.  18 = [ ] (6)

Nuffield Maths 2 Worksheets Pack 1

---

**Number 12**  name ........  date ........  sheet 2.2

This set of 10 counters has been divided into subsets with 2 counters in each.

There are [ 5 ] subsets.

The number sentence for this is: 10 = [ 5 ] (2)

This time each subset has 5 counters.

There are [ ] subsets.

10 = [ ] (5)

There are 8 stars, 4 in each subset.

[ ] subsets  8 = [ ] (4)

There are 8 stars, 2 in each subset.

[ ] subsets  8 = [ ] (2)

There are 12 triangles. Divide them into subsets with 4 triangles in each.

[ ] subsets  12 = [ ] (4)

There are 12 triangles. Divide them into subsets with 3 triangles in each.

[ ] subsets  12 = [ ] (3)

Nuffield Maths 2 Worksheets Pack 1

---

**Number 12**  name ........  date ........  sheet 2.3

Hopping back on the number line.

Start at 12.  Hop back in 2's until you reach 0.

0 1 2 3 4 5 6 7 8 9 10 11 12

It takes [ ] hops.  There are [ ] sets of 2 in 12.

Start at 15.  Hop back in 3's until you reach 0.

0 1 2 3 4 5 6 7 8 9 10 11 12 13 14 15

It takes [ ] hops.  There are [ ] sets of 3 in 15.

Start at 15.  Hop back in 5's until you reach 0.

0 1 2 3 4 5 6 7 8 9 10 11 12 13 14 15

It takes [ ] hops.  There are [ ] sets of 5 in 15.

Start at 14.  Hop back in 2's until you reach 0.

0 1 2 3 4 5 6 7 8 9 10 11 12 13 14

It takes [ ] hops.  There are [ ] sets of 2 in 14.

Start at 18.  Hop back in 3's until you reach 0.

0 1 2 3 4 5 6 7 8 9 10 11 12 13 14 15 16 17 18

It takes [ ] hops.  There are [ ] sets of 3 in 18.

Nuffield Maths 2 Worksheets Pack 1

---

**Number 12**  name ........  date ........  sheet 2.4

This strip is 10 squares long.

Colour the strip in 2's.

How many 2's are there? [ ]

10 = [ ] (2)

This strip is 15 squares long. Colour it in 5's.

How many 5's are there? [ ]

15 = [ ] (5)

This strip is 16 squares long. Colour it in 4's.

How many 4's are there? [ ]

16 = [ ] (4)

Nuffield Maths 2 Worksheets Pack 1

---

### N12 : 3  Division as the inverse of multiplication

Dealing with objects in practical situations, the two aspects of division (sharing and repeated subtraction) present two different types of problem. In both cases, however, division is the inverse of multiplication. In other words, division 'undoes' what is done by multiplication. At this stage teachers may wish to introduce the symbol $\div$ to be read as *divided by*, so that:

$2 \times \square = 8$ can be written as $8 \div 2 = \square$

$\square \times 4 = 8$ can be written as $8 \div 4 = \square$

This is very similar to the way in which subtraction 'undoes' what is done by addition.

$5 + \square = 8$ can be written as $8 - 5 = \square$

$\square + 3 = 8$ can be written as $8 - 3 = \square$

When counters are arranged in a rectangular array, the problem 'If 15

are put into 3 equal rows, how many in each row?' can be expressed as
$3(\square) = 15$ or $15 \div 3 = \square$; whereas the problem 'If 15 are put 5 in a row,
how many rows will there be?' can be expressed as $\square(5) = 15$ or
$15 \div 5 = \square$.

In the case of multiplication, the number of rows and the number of
columns are known. The problem involves finding the product—the total
number in the array. In the case of division, the total number in the array
and either the number of rows or columns are known. The problem
involves finding the missing factor—either the number of columns or the
number of rows.

Example:

18 counters placed 3 in a column:

How many in a row?
$3 \times \square = 18$ or $18 \div 3 = \square$

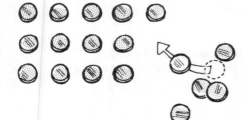

The multiplication square idea used in Chapter 5 can also be used 'in
reverse' for division.

| X | 1 | 2 | 3 | 4 | 5 | 6 |
|---|---|---|---|---|---|---|
| 1 | 1 | 2 | 3 | 4 | 5 | 6 |
| 2 | 2 | 4 | 6 | 8 | 10 | 12 |
| 3 | 3 | 6 | 9 | (12) | 15 | 18 |
| 4 | 4 | 8 | 12 | 16 | 20 | 24 |
| 5 | 5 | 10 | 15 | 20 | 25 | 30 |
| 6 | 6 | 12 | 18 | 24 | 30 | 36 |

Because
$12 = 4 \times 3$ and $12 = 3 \times 4$,
$12 \div 4 = 3$ and $12 \div 3 = 4$

(Note that the zeros have been
omitted in order to avoid the
complication of dividing by 0.)

*Worksheets should not be introduced
until children have had plenty of
practical experience
and opportunity for discussion.*

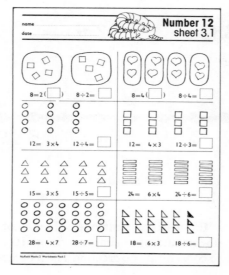

### N12 : 4   Remainders

If division is used in real-life situations, remainders are bound to arise. At this stage, it is advisable to restrict activity with most children to the discussion and informal recording of remainders.
Example :

Share 14 sweets between 3 children.

Each child has 4 sweets and there are 2 sweets remaining. It is important to point out that there are not enough left to give one more sweet to each child. Alternatively, this could be described as :

4 in each subset and 2 in the remainder set.

$14 \div 3 = 4$, remainder 2

How many children can be given 3 sweets each from 13 sweets?
4 children receive 3 sweets each and there is 1 remaining (not enough to give 3 to another child).

$13 \div 3 = 4$, remainder 1

Another method of recording is :

$13 = 3 \times 4 + 1$

but many children may find this difficult because two operations are involved—multiplication and addition.

When arranging counters into arrays, the remainder is shown, in the words of one boy, as 'The bit that sticks out and spoils the oblong.'
For example :

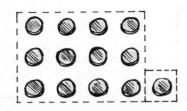

Arrange 13 counters in rows of 4.
How many rows are there?
Are any counters left over?
There are 3 rows of 4 and 1 counter over.

Some children may be able to use a 'counting on in fours' technique to get as close as possible to 13 without 'going over the top': 4, 8, 12
Three lots of 4 and 1 left over.

This idea may be illustrated by hopping back on a number line :

Not enough left for another hop, so 1 is the remainder.

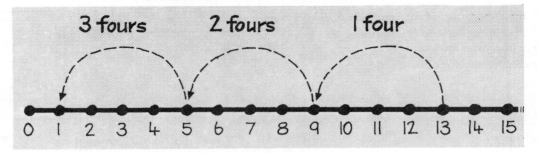

$13 \div 4 = 3$, remainder 1

Emphasis on remainders should not be allowed to cloud the child's understanding of simple division. It is much more important at this stage to concentrate on creating a firm base to be built up on later.

*Worksheets should not be introduced until children have had plenty of practical experience and opportunity for discussion.*

## References and resources

Nuffield Mathematics Teaching Project, *Computation and Structure* ③,
Nuffield Guide, Chambers/Murray 1967 (See Introduction page vii)

Shuard, H. and Williams, E. M. *Primary Mathematics Today*, Longman
Group UK Ltd 1976

E. J. Arnold *Multilink Number Track, Stern Number Track*

Osmiroid, *Centicube Number Track (Metline)*

Philip & Tacey Ltd, *Unifix Multiplication/Division Markers*

# Chapter 7
# Length (L2)

National Curriculum
Attainment Target 2: Level 2
Attainment Target 2: Level 4
Attainment Target 8: Level 2
Attainment Target 8: Level 3
Attainment Target 13: Level 2
Attainment Target 13: Level 3

## For the teacher

This chapter builds on and extends the ideas introduced in Chapter 7 (Length 1) of *Nuffield Maths 1 Teachers' Handbook*. Having used arbitrary units such as straws, pencils and parts of the body, the children are taken a stage further in appreciating the need for a standard unit. Activities involving longer/shorter than, taller/shorter than and wider/narrower than are repeated, this time making the comparison first with the metre and then with the 10 centimetre rod. Measuring in centimetres and the use of calibrated rulers provides opportunities to reinforce work done on the number line.

It is important not to restrict the measurement of length to one plane or direction. Height, depth, width, girth, perimeter, circumference, straight and curved lines should be included.

## Summary of the stages

**L2**: 1    Appreciating the need for a standard measure

**L2**: 2    Introduction of the metre

**L2**: 3    Comparison with a 10 cm rod (decimetre)

**L2**: 4    Measuring in centimetres—straight and curved lines

**L2**: 5    Personal measurements in m and cm

## Vocabulary

Long/short, wide/narrow, thick/thin, tall/short, high/low, deep/shallow and their comparatives and superlatives, length, width, breadth, height, circumference, perimeter, metre, decimetre, centimetre.

Note that the abbreviation for metre(s) is m and the abbreviation for centimetre(s) is cm and no full stops are required unless at the end of a sentence.

## Equipment and apparatus

Metre sticks, plain and calibrated in cm; 10 cm rods, rulers 10, 20, 30 cm plain and calibrated in cm; measuring tapes, 1 m and 10 m lengths of thick string or rope, height measures.

## Working with the children

### L2: 1   Appreciating the need for a standard measure

If several children have measured the length of the classroom in paces (or the width of a corridor using 'heel and toe' measurement, or the length of a table in hand spans, etc.) comparison of their results will lead to the question, 'If we have all measured the same distance, why aren't the results all the same?' Some children may insist that a mistake has been made in the counting. When a repetition of the measuring exercise still gives differing results, another line of argument may follow. In one case the answer came back, 'It's not fair 'cause John's got longer legs than Alan.' The 'not fair' argument can be used by the teacher to lead the children to see that a measure is needed that is the same for everyone. A metre is a metre whether it is used by a giant or a midget!

*Worksheets should not be introduced until children have had plenty of practical experience and opportunity for discussion.*

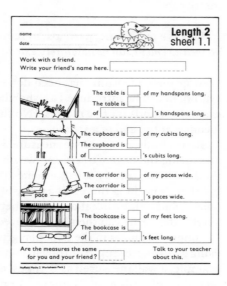

### L2: 2   Introduction of the metre

In the first instance uncalibrated rules or sticks which are 1 metre long (dead length) should be used. Several lengths of rope each 1 metre long are also useful as they can be 'folded' to measure parts of a metre. The children must be given plenty of opportunity to handle the metre sticks or ropes and to find objects which are longer than, shorter than or about 1 metre in length. They may find out how many of their own handspans, foot or 'cubit' measures there are in a metre.

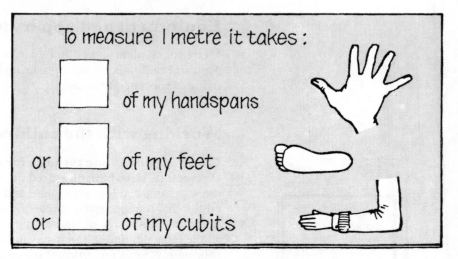

As they become familiar with and can visualize the metre length, children should be encouraged to make estimates first and then to measure the length and width of the classroom, corridor, etc. It is not advisable to attempt to measure heights of more than 2 metres.

When discussing, and later recording, these measurements, such phrases as 'about 3 metres', 'just over 4 metres', 'nearly 5 metres' or 'about 3 and half metres' are used. The 'bits left over' can be estimated by using the metre rope:

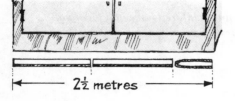

This is a good time, perhaps, to remind children that, unlike counting, *no measurement can be absolutely exact.*

After some recording has been done using 'metre' or 'metres' in full, the symbol m can be introduced as 'shorthand' for either, so that 5 m, for example, stands for five metres. (No full stop is required after the m unless it comes at the end of a sentence.)

Some children are able to measure an object but are less confident when measuring the distance *between* two objects, for example, the distance from the door to the teacher's desk. As one girl protested, 'I can't measure it—there's nothing there!' If a piece of string is stretched between the objects and either cut off or nipped between the fingers at the required length, the string can then be measured with a metre stick.

Longer distances in the hall, playground or corridor can be measured by using a 10-metre length of rope in conjunction with a metre rule. For example, a wall measured as 2 'ropes' and 4 metre sticks would lead to the recording of (20 + 4) or 24 metres. Long measuring tapes can be used but they often lead to the children being confused by the markings. If a trundle wheel is used, the teacher should make sure that the child really appreciates that a 'click' denotes 1 metre, perhaps by 'testing' the trundle wheel on a known length. Many children cannot connect counting 'clicks' with measuring length.

*Worksheets should not be introduced until children have had plenty of practical experience and opportunity for discussion.*

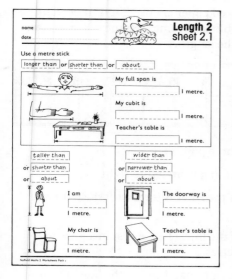

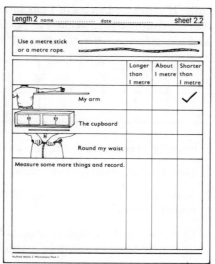

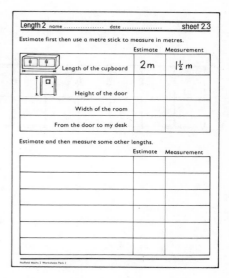

**L2 : 3    Comparison with a 10-centimetre rod (decimetre)**
The 10-centimetre rod (dead length and unmarked, such as an orange Cuisenaire rod), is a useful unit for measuring many items like desks, chairs, books and shelves for which the metre is too long. The name *decimetre* can be introduced—especially when the children have placed 10 end to end to make up 1 metre.

It is not intended that the decimetre should become a commonly used measure. It is introduced at this stage because its handy size enables children to gain further experience of a repeated standard unit without having to deal with large numbers of centimetre units.

*Worksheets should not be introduced until children have had plenty of practical experience and opportunity for discussion.*

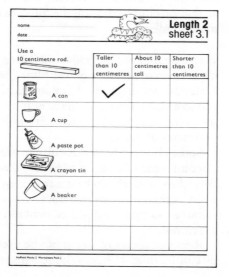

## L2: 4 Measurement in centimetres—straight and curved lines

Some children experience difficulty in using a calibrated ruler. It helps if they use 'dead length' rulers—that is those without extra pieces on the ends. If calibrated strips of 1 cm squared paper are used, it is important that the numerals are as close as possible to the lines. Numerals in spaces lead to confusion when 'reading off' the length.

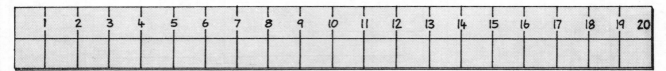

Initially, it is useful to emphasize these points:

1  Use the ruler with the numerals reading from left to right.

2  Make sure that the left hand end of the ruler is level with the left hand end of the line.

3  Count along the ruler to the end of the line. (In the first instance, use lines with lengths in whole centimetres.)

4  Read off the numeral level with the right hand end of the line. This is the length of the line in centimetres.

5  Write down the length. (Many children become so engrossed in the measuring that they forget to record.)

Children need plenty of practice in using a calibrated ruler—measuring lines, Cuisenaire or Colour Factor rods, strips of card, sticks, the edges of boxes, etc. Some children will omit stage 3 and read off without counting along. Gradually, they will gain confidence until they are ready to attempt measuring longer lines and objects. The same basic points apply except that stage 3 will involve counting in tens first then the odd units at the end. For example, 10, 20, 30 and 4, that is 34 centimetres.

Measuring curved lengths involves the use of an intermediate measure—a piece of string. The children first lay the string carefully on the curved line (again, ensuring that the starting ends are level) and nip the string with their finger nails level with the other end of the line. They then transfer the string, carefully gripping the 'nip', to a ruler in order to read off the measurement.

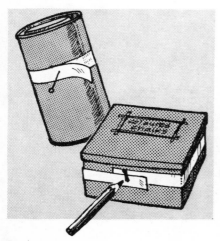

*Perimeter and circumference*  Children may have heard the word perimeter mentioned in prisoner of war films (perimeter fence) or in connection with athletics (perimeter track) or airfields. The idea of a fence or boundary round a shape is a good one to emphasize when introducing perimeter to mean the distance all round. Circumference is a special name given to the perimeter of a circle.

Some children have difficulty in measuring a perimeter or circumference. If a strip of paper is wrapped tightly around the outside of a tin or box, a mark can be made somewhere on the overlap using a pencil or a pin pushed through two thicknesses of the paper. The strip is then removed so that the distance between pencil marks or pin-holes can be measured.

Ropes or pieces of string can be used to measure the girth of trees, the circumferences of hoops, large balls, etc.

Structural apparatus which is based on a centimetre unit (for example, Cuisenaire, Colour Factor or Centicubes), can be used to provide extra practice in measuring in centimetres. These activities will also reinforce number work if, after measuring and recording, the child either performs the appropriate computation or uses his knowledge of number bonds to check the result.

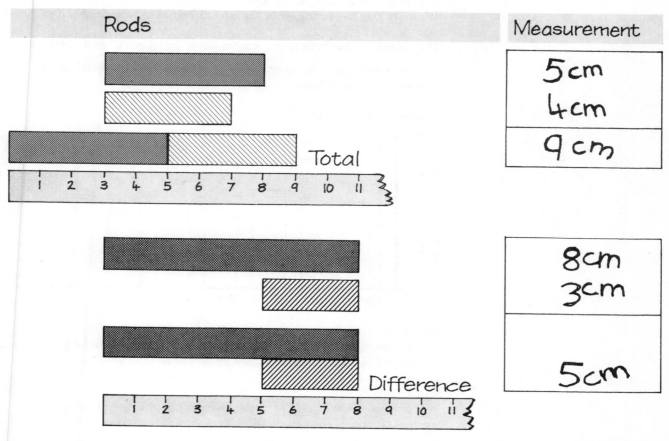

## Rods

## Measurement

5cm
4cm
9cm

Total

8cm
3cm

5cm

Difference

*Worksheets should not be introduced until children have had plenty of practical experience and opportunity for discussion.*

## L2 : 5   Personal measurements in metres and centimetres

By filling in the 'All about me' sheets (Worksheet L2 : 5.1) the children gain further measuring experience. It is suggested that the children work in threes or fours using rulers, measuring tapes and height measures.

Once completed, the 'All about me' sheets provide many opportunities for discussion about length :

'Is your height greater, less or about the same as your arm span ?'
'Which is longer—your pace or the circumference of your head ? How much longer ?'
'How many of your little finger lengths make the length of your cubit ?' etc.

Graphs will help to focus on the range of measurements which occur within a group of children.

*Handspans on red table*

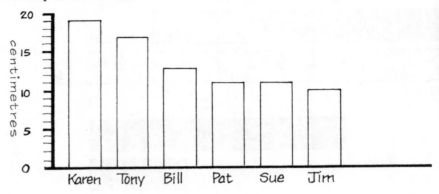

Which child has the largest handspan ?
What is the difference between the largest and the smallest handspans ?
Which two children have handspans about the same length ? etc.

*Worksheets should not be introduced until children have had plenty of practical experience and opportunity for discussion.*

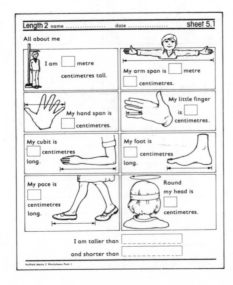

80

# References and resources

Burke, P. and Albany, E. *Mini's log cabin*, Bronto Books Set E, Nuffield Maths 5–11, Longman Group UK Ltd 1979

Nuffield Teaching Project, *Beginnings* ▽, Checking up 2, Computation and Structure ②, Nuffield Guides, Chambers/Murray 1967 (See Introduction page vii)

Shuard, H. and Williams, E. M. *Primary Mathematics Today*, Longman Group UK Ltd 1976

E. J. Arnold, *100 cm Rule, Roll up Height Measure, Set of Metre Sticks First Metre Rod*

Nicolas Burdett Ltd, *10 m Wall Measure, Calliper, Flexible Height Measure, Height Measure and Floor Stand, Measuring Tapes, Set of Metre Sticks*

Osmiroid, *10 m Tape Measure, Depth Gauge, Graduated Callipers*

Philip & Tacey Ltd, *1 Metre Graduated Paper Strips, Metre Measuring and Comparison Rods Set, Metre Measuring Tapes, Metric-Aid Metre Tape, Metric Measuring Scale*

Taskmaster, *Flexible 1 m Measures, Measuring Tapes, Metre Rules*

# Chapter 8
# Shape and space (S2)

National Curriculum
Attainment Target 10: Level 1
Attainment Target 10: Level 2
Attainment Target 10: Level 3
Attainment Target 11: Level 2
Attainment Target 12: Level 1

## For the teacher

Among the important purposes for the study of the properties of space, E. M. Williams and H. Shuard list the following:

Through his own inventiveness a child will learn to appreciate the patterns and forms which men have used for decoration and enjoyment.

Different kinds of manipulation of shapes involve some operations which are common to all kinds of mathematical activity; sorting, combining, partitioning, matching, ordering, and the fundamental types of movement.'

*Primary Mathematics Today* Longman Group UK Ltd

By building on and extending the work begun in Chapter 8 of *Nuffield Maths 1 Teachers' Handbook*, this chapter uses observation of the environment and structured activities to provide children with valuable and relevant experience in appreciating and handling shape.

Particular emphasis is given to an informal approach to area by using arbitrary units to cover surfaces.

## Summary of the stages

**S2**: 1    Sorting for shape and size

**S2**: 2    Fitting shapes together

**S2**: 3    Surfaces and faces

**S2**: 4    Covering surfaces—leading to area

**S2**: 5    First ideas of symmetry

**S2**: 6    Angles and rotation

# Vocabulary

Same, shape, square, oblong, rectangle*, circle, triangle, equilateral, pentagon, hexagon, octagon, regular, overlap, fit together, gaps, spaces.

Cube, cuboid, cylinder, sphere, cone, prism, pyramid, triangular, hexagonal, solid, hollow.

Surface, face, skin, peel, edge, corners, flat, curved, straight, rough, smooth, shiny, dull, cover, area.

Balance, line of balance, symmetry, axis of symmetry, symmetrical, 'back to front', 'upside down', mirror, quarter, half, left, right, forward, back, angle, right angle, turn (rotate), reflect (flipover), translate (slide).

*Squares and oblongs are both rectangles. The word oblong may be used for those rectangles which do not have four equal sides.

# Equipment and apparatus

A large selection of solid, hollow and flat shapes: building blocks, Lego, Poleidoblocs, construction sets, boxes, cartons and containers of all sorts, cylinders, beads, balls, hoops.

Plastic tiles, stiff cardboard shapes, lino pieces, vinyl floor tiles, pictures of shapes, attribute blocks, plasticine, clay, dough, etc., squared paper (5 cm 2 cm), geoboards and rubber bands, pegboards and pegs, small mirrors (preferably unbreakable plastic).

# Working with the children

### S2: 1   Sorting for shape and size

Once the children can recognize and are familiar with the names of the 2-dimensional shapes introduced in Chapter 8 of *Teachers' Handbook 1* (squares, oblongs, rectangles, circles and triangles), they can begin to match pairs of each shape which are of the same size. Using plastic tiles or shapes cut from vinyl, lino or thick card, make a collection of about six of each of the four shapes with only two of each shape the same size. The child selects a shape and then has to find the one that matches it exactly. He can record by placing the pairs on a piece of manilla card prepared as follows:

This activity enables him to handle the pair of shapes in order to satisfy himself that one fits exactly on the other. Discussion about the activity should bring out such points as:

The square and the oblong are both rectangles and both have four sides.
The triangle has three sides. Can triangles be of a different shape?
The circle has a curved side; all the others have straight sides.

This may be a good opportunity to introduce plane shapes with more than four sides—the pentagon (five sides), the hexagon (six sides), and the octagon (eight sides). Most commercially produced sets of shapes tend to include only the *regular* versions of these shapes, with all the sides equal and all the angles equal.

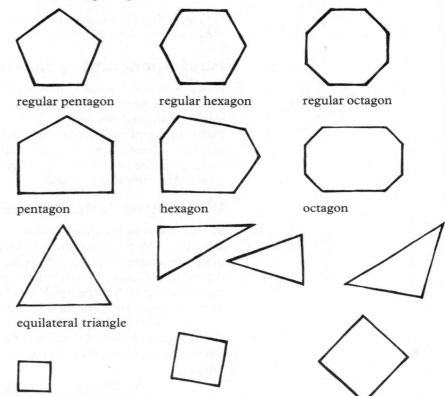

regular pentagon       regular hexagon       regular octagon

pentagon       hexagon       octagon

It is important that children realize that a five-sided figure, for instance, is called a pentagon whether its sides are equal or not.

equilateral triangle

This of course is also true of triangles. In this case, the regular triangle is usually called equilateral.

It is also important to illustrate and emphasize that the name of a shape does not depend on its size or its orientation.

Children need plenty of opportunity to handle plane shapes made from stiff card, plastic or cut from lino or vinyl tiles. Activities should include matching for shape and size and sorting by counting the number of sides.

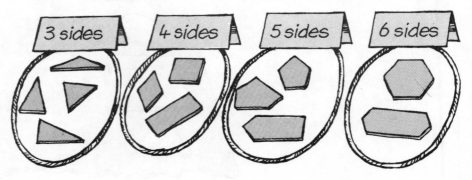

If several plane shapes of the same shape and size are made, the idea of a prism can be illustrated by piling or aligning them to make a solid. At this stage, the prism can be thought of as a solid which could be cut into parallel slices all the same shape and size. This cannot be done in the case of a sphere, a cone, or a 'cottage loaf'.

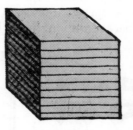
rectangular prism
or cuboid

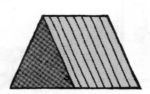
triangular prism

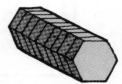
hexagonal prism

*Worksheets should not be introduced until children have had plenty of practical experience and opportunity for discussion.*

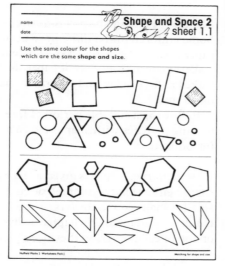

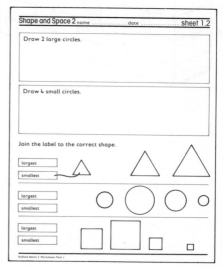

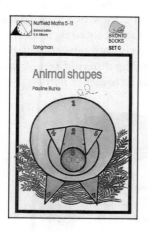

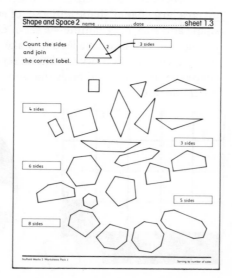

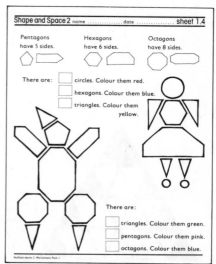

## S2: 2a  Fitting shapes together—three-dimensional shapes

Further experience of junk modelling (see Chapter 8 of *Teachers'
Handbook 1*) and packing bricks into boxes will lead children to appreciate
that some three-dimensional shapes fit together better than others.
Examples from the environment such as brick walls, sugar lumps in a box,
soap packets in a carton, etc., can be compared with the way in which eggs,
sticks of chalk or marbles are packed in a box. This will show that shapes
which can be packed without spaces between them are better 'space fillers'.

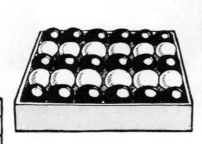

## S2: 2b  Fitting shapes together—two-dimensional shapes

Some children find it difficult to fit together plane shapes made from thin
paper because there is always a tendency to overlap. When a boy was asked to
make a pattern from a set of paper shapes but not to overlap the edges, he
looked at his teacher and said rather patronisingly, 'No, I won't overlap—I'll
underlap.'

Following a suitable period of free-play with large and small mosaic tiles,
making pictures with shapes etc., a more structured programme may be
introduced.

*First activity*  A child is given a large paper shape and an assortment of
shapes either ready-gummed or cut from wallpaper and asked to stick the
smaller shapes on to the large shape in order to cover it entirely. Young
children tend to do this haphazardly, sticking shapes anywhere and often
on top of each other, so they need plenty of guidance and practice.

*Second activity*  Working either individually or in pairs, the children are
given a large paper shape and a set of smaller shapes which are all alike in
shape and size, for example—a set of circles, a set of squares, a set of
triangles, etc. They are asked to make a pattern without overlapping any of
the shapes. This activity should be repeated using different sets of smaller
shapes so that the child finds that some shapes fit together without gaps but
others do not.

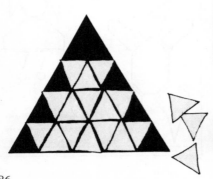

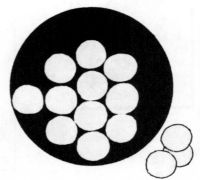

The children should be encouraged to look for examples of shapes in the environment which fit together without gaps—square tiled walls, brickwork, window panes, floor tiles and parquet floors, pictures of honeycombs, etc.

The experience gained from this sort of tiling or tessellation, covering a surface completely by using units which are all the same shape and size, is an important preparation for the measurement of area. The measurement of length is dependent upon the fact that units of length placed end to end on a line make an aggregate or total length.

5 units of length

Similarly the measurement of area is dependent upon the fact that units of area, when tessellated, make an aggregate or total area.

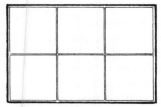

6 units of area

*Worksheets should not be introduced until children have had plenty of practical experience and opportunity for discussion.*

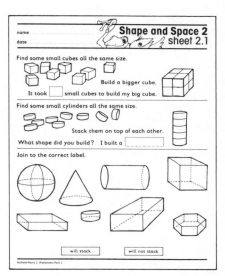

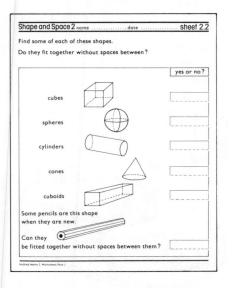

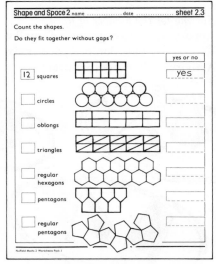

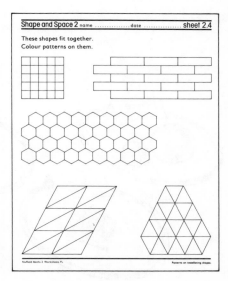

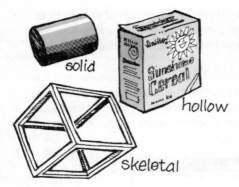

solid

hollow

skeletal

## S2: 3   Surfaces and faces

Through handling three-dimensional objects such as bricks, boxes, balls, cones, etc., the child will have begun to experience the difference between flat and curved surfaces. Of the three types of three-dimensional model which the children may have handled: solid, hollow, skeletal, the skeletal model has the advantage of showing the space inside but when wishing to draw attention to *faces*, obviously the solid or hollow models are more appropriate.

As well as looking at surfaces which are flat or curved and large or small (the floor of the hall compared with the face of a cube), it is useful to compare the *textures* of surfaces. For example, paper has a smooth surface; a metal tray a shiny surface; a polystyrene tile a rough surface, etc.

*Activities and experiences involved*

Touch table—A collection of materials displaying different surfaces e.g. rough, smooth, sticky, lumpy, prickly, shiny, dull, furry, fluffy, etc.

Making different textured surfaces by covering with various materials— paint, chalk, paper, lentils, egg shells, pasta, paste mixed with sawdust, string, tissue paper twists, etc. Stress covering the *whole surface*.

Covering a table with paper in preparation for craftwork.

Looking at large surfaces, such as playgrounds, hall floors and comparing sizes.

Handling 3-dimensional solids for experience of both flat and curved surfaces.

Some children may not yet realize that a face of a solid is a surface bounded by edges. The activities mentioned in Chapter 8 of *Nuffield Maths 1 Teachers' Handbook*, such as drawing round a box to make a picture of the face put on the paper or 'peeling off' the faces of a solid which has had a paper 'skin' loosely affixed to it, will help in this respect.

Another useful activity is to colour each face of a solid with a different coloured chalk, paint or crayon. Before crossing over each edge the colour must be changed because a new face is to be covered. It is interesting to watch children doing this, especially if they start with a cube or cuboid, then a cylinder, then a cone and, finally, a sphere. Since no edges are crossed on the sphere, only one colour is used so it has only one 'face'!

*Sorting for the number of faces*

Apparatus: An assortment of small wooden bricks (including Poleidoblocs), five or six hoops, pieces of coloured chalk.

Activity:    The hoops are laid out on the floor and labelled:

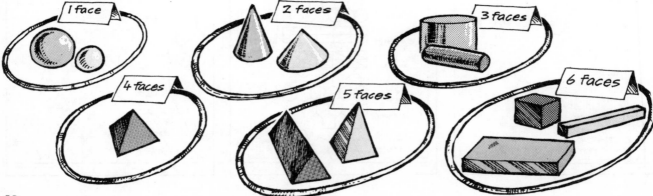

Two or three children are asked to count the number of faces on each brick and then put it in the correct hoop. Each child is given a piece of chalk and as he counts each face he chalks on the brick the number of faces he has counted. For example, on a cube he will write the numbers 1, 2, 3, 4, 5, 6. Often children tend to forget where they began and count one face twice or they miss counting some faces altogether. The marking of the faces acts as a check for the child and avoids any confusion. If each child uses a different colour chalk, the teacher knows who is responsible should one brick be placed in the wrong hoop.

The children should be encouraged to learn and use the correct names for these shapes:

1 face  –  sphere
2 faces  –  cone
3 faces  –  cylinder
4 faces  –  triangular pyramid
5 faces  –  square pyramid
               triangular prism
6 faces  –  cube, cuboid

This sorting may be extended to looking for portable solids in the classroom which can be categorized in the same way. Pictures cut from newspapers, magazines or from books can also be collected to make 'A book of cuboids', etc.

After counting the *number* of faces, the children should also be encouraged to look at the *types* of face a solid has. Drawing round the faces, taking cardboard boxes and containers apart or the 'peeling off the skin' idea are all useful activities.

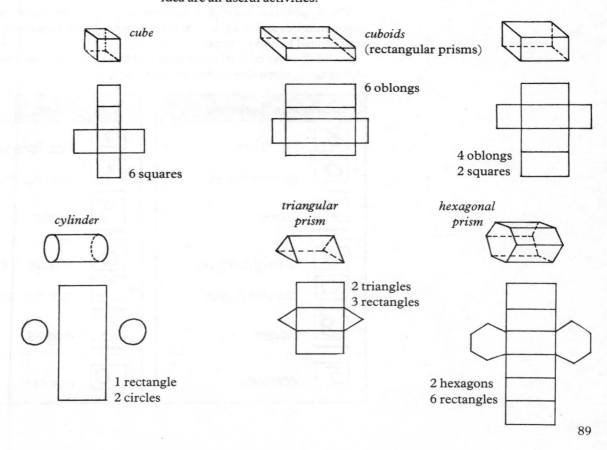

*cube*

6 squares

*cuboids*
(rectangular prisms)

6 oblongs

4 oblongs
2 squares

*cylinder*

1 rectangle
2 circles

*triangular prism*

2 triangles
3 rectangles

*hexagonal prism*

2 hexagons
6 rectangles

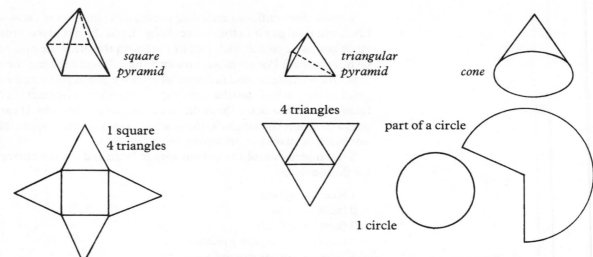

square
pyramid

triangular
pyramid

cone

1 square
4 triangles

4 triangles

part of a circle

1 circle

The *sphere* presents a problem which is perhaps best illustrated by trying to remove the peel of an orange in one piece!

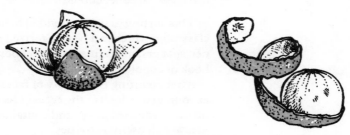

The Appendix at the end of this chapter gives the names of the more common solids and dealing with the problem of depicting three-dimensional figures on paper.

Each solid may be further investigated by looking at edges and corners as well as faces, using sheets like this for recording:

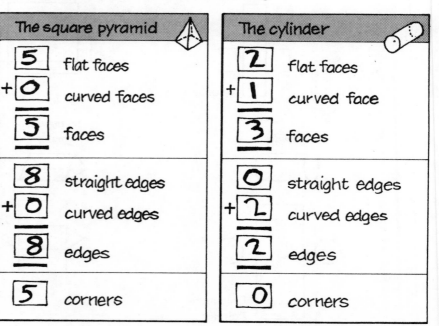

| The square pyramid | |
|---|---|
| 5 | flat faces |
| + 0 | curved faces |
| 5 | faces |
| 8 | straight edges |
| + 0 | curved edges |
| 8 | edges |
| 5 | corners |

| The cylinder | |
|---|---|
| 2 | flat faces |
| + 1 | curved face |
| 3 | faces |
| 0 | straight edges |
| + 2 | curved edges |
| 2 | edges |
| 0 | corners |

*Worksheets should not be introduced until children have had plenty of practical experience and opportunity for discussion.*

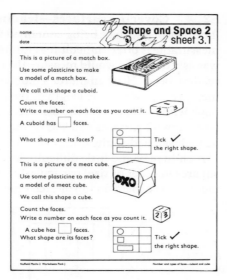

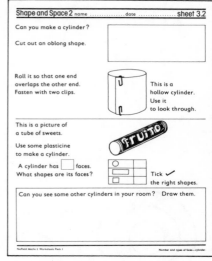

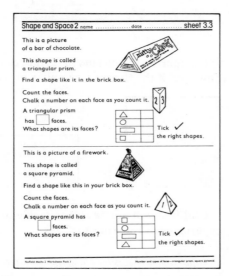

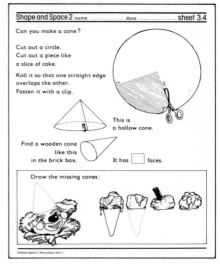

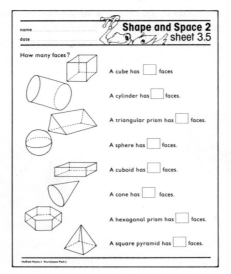

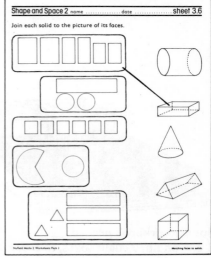

### S2 : 4   Covering surfaces—leading to area

The idea of a surface being contained within a boundary and therefore measurable is often difficult for children to understand. A six-year-old boy was asked how he would measure the surface of the front cover of his reading book. He thought for a moment then took a ruler and began to measure repeatedly the length of the cover, moving across the width of the book with no regard for the distances between each measure. He was familiar with surfaces and was trying to apply the sort of measuring device he had watched adults use.

A child may find little difficulty in putting a collection of circles or squares in order of size, particularly if there is a marked difference. He may merely place them on top of each other.

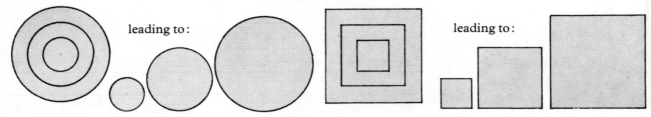

Comparing the *amount of surface* or *area* of shapes presents problems, however, if the shapes are unlike or irregular.

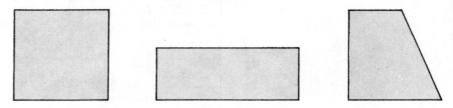

Children will not be able to tackle these until they have had plenty of experience of covering surfaces.

*Comparing surfaces by covering—practical activities*   Initially children seem happiest using three-dimensional objects to cover the surfaces being compared. In effect, a single face of each covering object is being used as a 'tile'. For instance, when comparing John's workbook and Sandra's reading book, John's book was wider but Sandra's was longer so to compare the surface areas, various tins and boxes were used to cover them.

John's workbook needed
1 crayon tin, 2 chalk boxes, to cover it.

Sandra's reading book needed
1 crayon tin, 2 chalk boxes, 3 match boxes, to cover it.

The surface of John's book is smaller than Sandra's. Sandra's book has a greater area than John's.

Comparing pairs of surfaces using a variety of measuring units tends to be time consuming and inaccurate so the next step is to collect sets of covering units of different sizes, such as matchboxes, cigarette packets, cereal packets, soap powder boxes, balsa bricks, tobacco tins, egg boxes, etc. Objects all the same size are now used as 'tiles' to cover the surface being measured. Some children may find it difficult to compare areas but still gain valuable experience by just fitting boxes together in order to 'measure' a surface.

*Directed activities* Apparatus: Sets of 3 dimensional objects as listed above. Assignment cards set out either in pictorial or written form. The teacher should always check that the child understands his assignment before he begins.

*The bit left over* After some experience in covering surfaces, children will learn to choose a suitable covering unit for the job. Not all areas to be covered require a whole number of units—some have awkward gaps and corners which defy all the children's deftness in manipulating the chosen set of measuring units. In the end children either ignore the uncovered part or refer to it as 'a bit', saying, 'It takes ten boxes and a bit.' At this point the teacher can help by discussing the estimations with the children. Again, much will depend on the stage the children's thinking has reached.

This may be the opportunity to introduce sets of paper shapes to use for covering. Two-dimensional rectangular shapes can be used to cover as much of the area as possible and, where necessary, cut up to fit into the gaps. The cut pieces can then be put together again in order to give a more accurate measurement of the area.

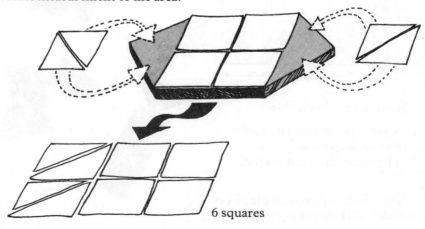

6 squares

Once a child has acquired some facility in the covering of surfaces, he should be encouraged to put various dissimilar shapes in order of area. This he can do by measuring their areas using either sets of 3-D objects or 2-D shapes as measuring units. Only two surfaces should be compared to begin with. The areas to be compared should not be too different in size so that the child may use the same measuring unit for both.

Duplicated sheets like this may be used:

It takes ☐ ....... to cover ............
It takes ☐ ....... to cover ............
The surface of [⎯⎯⎯⎯⎯⎯⎯⎯⎯]
is ............ than
the surface of [⎯⎯⎯⎯⎯⎯⎯⎯⎯]

It takes ☐ **squares** to cover a P.E. mat.
It takes ☐ **squares** to cover the door mat.
The surface of [⎯⎯⎯⎯⎯⎯⎯⎯⎯]
is ... **greater** ... than
the surface of [⎯⎯⎯⎯⎯⎯⎯⎯⎯]

The teacher fills in the details
for a particular assignment.

The child fills in the gaps
as he completes each part.

*Conservation of area* It is important that children should realize that the same amount of area can appear in many different surface shapes. As with most ideas connected with the concept of area, this may take some time to develop. The following activity, a simplified version of the ancient Chinese Tangram, will provide valuable experience for children.

A square of card or vinyl floor tile, 4 cm by 4 cm, is cut into pieces as shown in this diagram:

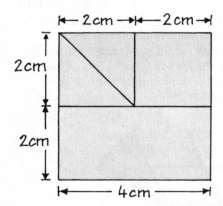

There are two simple rules:

1  All four pieces must be used to
   make a new shape.
2  The pieces must not overlap.

The children rearrange the pieces
to make other shapes or figures.

These may be recorded by colouring 2 cm graph paper or using sticky shapes on plain paper.

This activity may also be used by the teacher as a check-up on the child's level of understanding of conservation of area.

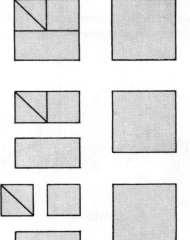

Place one of the simple tangrams on the table beside a 4 cm × 4 cm square of card.

Ask the child if the cards cover the same amount of the table. If he says 'Yes', split the tangram into two parts and ask if the two pieces cover the same amount of table as the whole card. If he says 'Yes', split the tangram again and repeat the question. If 'Yes', split again and repeat the question.

If at any stage the child says 'No', he requires further experience, at frequent intervals, with activities involving covering surface as outlined earlier in this chapter.

*Area and perimeter* It is frequently noted that some children (even the clever ones) find it difficult to establish the difference between *area* and *perimeter*. The activities suggested in this section should help children to associate area with *covering* a surface using flat boxes, tiles, paper shapes, etc. Perimeter, or 'around measure', should suggest a piece of string acting as a boundary or 'fence' enclosing an area.

*Worksheets should not be introduced until children have had plenty of practical experience and opportunity for discussion.*

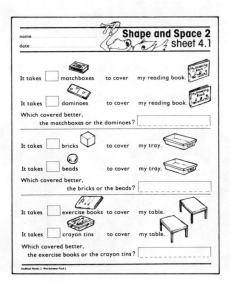

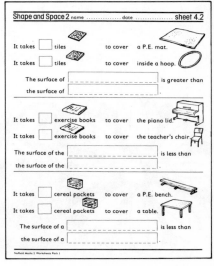

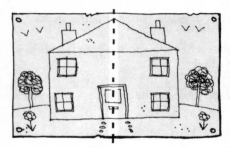

line of balance
(axis of symmetry)

## S2 : 5  First ideas of symmetry

Children seem to have a natural feeling for symmetry and use it intuitively in their art and constructional play—their pictures and models tend to be symmetrical. They are probably not familiar with the word *symmetry*, so initially the word *balance* could be used to describe a shape or picture which is 'alike on both sides' of the line of balance.

When the line of balance is vertical, the children sometimes call this 'back to front'; when the line of balance or *axis of symmetry* is horizontal, they may use 'upside down'.

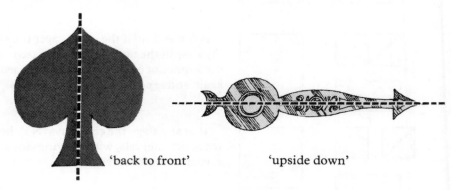

'back to front'　　　　　'upside down'

In their art work children appear to have little difficulty in producing both 'back to front' and 'upside down' symmetry within the same pattern.

There are many examples of shapes in the environment which display the property of balance.

A car is balanced this way . . . but not this way.

Symmetry in nature is often overlooked by children and their attention should be drawn to the balance of flowers, certain leaves and insects.

## Activities

*Blot patterns* Fold a piece of paper down the middle.
Open out and put a blob of paint on the fold.
Fold the paper again and carefully press down on the paper.
Open out and let paint dry. The picture will display a back to front pattern with the axis running along the fold of the paper.

*String patterns* Fold a piece of paper in half.
Cover a piece of string with paint.
Open paper and place string on one half, near the fold, leaving one end of the string over the edge of the paper.
Place one hand firmly on the folded paper and pull the string out by the loose end.
Open up and allow paint to dry. The picture again will display a back to front pattern with the *axis of symmetry* running down the fold.

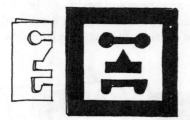

*Paper folding and cutting* Fold a piece of paper in half.
Cut a shape out of the double thickness.
When opened out and mounted on a coloured sheet, a symmetrical shape shows through.

If the paper is folded three or four times before cutting, several axes of symmetry can be shown:

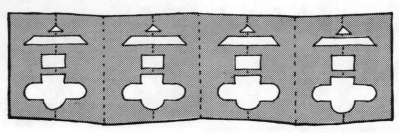

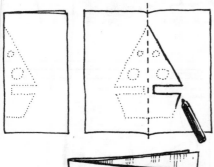

*Pin pricking and carbon patterns*
Fold a piece of paper in half.
Draw any shape on one side up to the fold.
Prick through the paper with a pin along the line of the drawn shape.
Open up the paper and draw over the pin holes.
Again, the *line of balance* or *axis of symmetry* is along the fold.

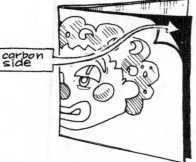

carbon side

A similar effect is obtained by folding a sheet of carbon paper with the carbon on the *outside*, placing it inside a paper 'cover' and drawing on the front of the 'cover'.
A symmetrical design will appear when the paper is opened out.

*Mirrors,* which can now be obtained in unbreakable plastic, are very useful for showing the symmetry of environmental shapes, geometrical shapes and letters.

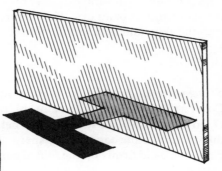
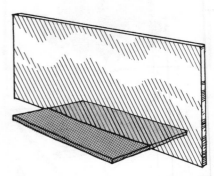

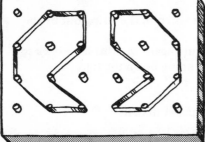

*Geoboards, pegboards etc.* A chalk line drawn on a geoboard is used as the axis of symmetry. Children use rubber bands to make symmetrical patterns or to make the 'other half' of a shape made by a partner.

Similar activities may be designed using: pegs and pegboard, beads threaded to make a symmetrical necklace, or centicubes on a baseboard. Here, colour as well as pattern must be considered to achieve complete balance.

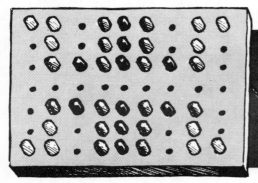
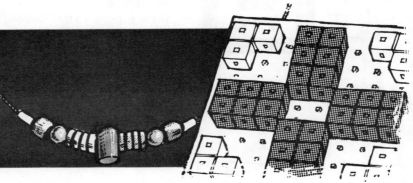

*Worksheets should not be introduced until children have had plenty of practical experience and opportunity for discussion.*

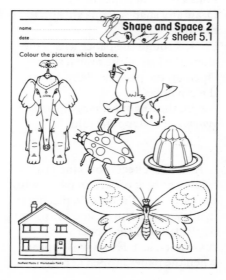

98

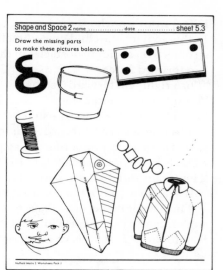

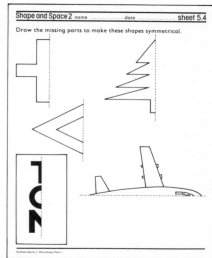

## S2:6  Angles and rotation

An angle indicates the amount of *turn or rotation* that has taken place.

   In order to appreciate this, children need experience of actually turning themselves. Initially, this can be done by giving simple instructions to face different directions in the classroom (front wall, the door side, back wall, the window side) by turning or rotating through a quarter or half of a complete turn.

For example:
'Start facing the front wall.'
'Now turn to face the door side.'
'You have made a quarter of a turn.'
'Now make another quarter turn to the right.'
'Which wall are you facing now?'

   The same idea can be used but with children as the four points of direction.
'If you start facing Anne, which way and how far must you turn to face Don?'
'Now what turn must you make in order to face Betty?'

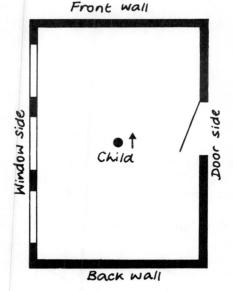

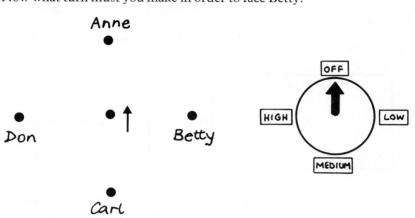

   In *worksheet 6.1* the same idea is used to select one of the four positions on the control knob of a cooker.

**Blind man's path**

In this activity one child gives directions to guide a blindfolded partner to an objective, avoiding obstacles in the way.

'Go forward 2 steps.'

'Turn right. Go forward 3 steps.'

'Turn left. Forward 2 steps.'

'Turn left again. Forward 1 step.'

   The journey can be recorded on squared paper using a simple scale (the side of a square representing one step) and written down in the form: FD2, RT, FD3, LT, FD2, LT, FD1.

'How many different ways are there of making the journey?'

   If available, LOGO can be used to reinforce this idea.

   The plan or model of a village or town, with streets intersecting at right angles, can be used to provide experience in giving directions (See the Bronto Book: *Left, right* or *worksheet 6.2.*)

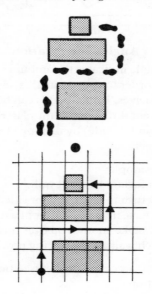

   The quarter turn or 'square corner' can be made by folding a piece of paper twice to make a 'square corner tester'. The children can use this to find as many 'square corners' as they can on windows, doors, books, posters, etc.

   The vertex of a cube or cuboid has three 'square corners'.

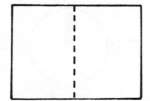 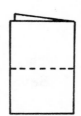  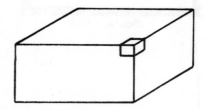

Care should be taken when introducing the term *right angle*. The word *right* can mean the opposite of *wrong* or the opposite of *left* but in this context it is linked with *upright* because vertical lines are at *right-angles* to horizontal lines. Some children may wonder why we cannot have left angles as well as right angles!

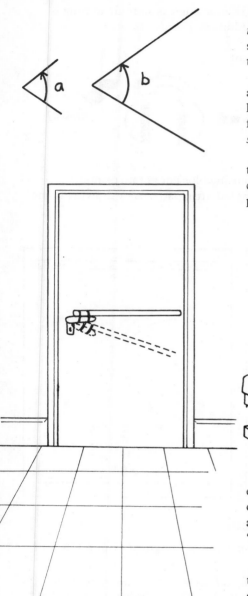

It is important that children realize that *an angle measures the amount of turn or rotation* that has taken place, otherwise they are likely to confuse the size of an angle with the length of its arms or even the distance between them.

For example, although its arms are longer, angle b is the same size as angle a. This can be demonstrated by taping a long thin stick to a door handle in order to emphasize that although the end of the stick moves farther than the end of the handle when it is turned, *the amount of turn is the same*.

Children should be encouraged to look for, draw and make a list of things that rotate through an angle: radio or television control knobs, doors, handles, hands of a clock, pointers on kitchen scales, a swinging pendulum, blades of a pair of scissors, jaw bones, pages of a book, etc.

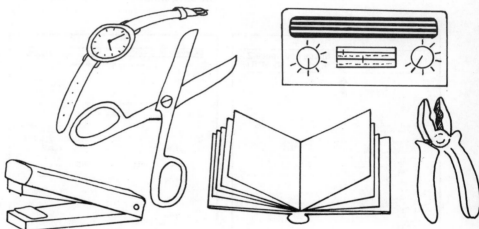

As well as these dynamic examples, children should also look for, estimate and compare static cases in addition to the right angles or 'square corners' they have already found. Classification into acute and obtuse angles will come at a later stage, but in the meantime, a useful device is the 'angle maker'.

Cut along a radius of two different coloured paper or card circles and put them together as shown in the diagram. Children can then estimate the size of an angle and make a copy of it. If transparent plastic is used for the circles, an angle can be copied by placing the 'angle maker' over the angle to be copied.

Alternatively, use a *Rotogram*. (See References and resources section at the end of this chapter.)

'Make the angle between the hands of a clock that says 3 o'clock.'

'Now show me the angle for 2 o'clock.'

'Now 11 o'clock.'

'Make the angle between your pointing finger and the next finger.'

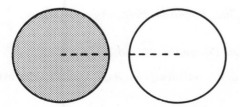
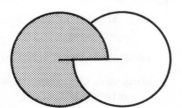
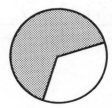

It is important to stress that every time an angle is altered, nothing is made longer or shorter but that something is *turned or rotated*.

Experience of three types of movement:

*translation* (sliding)
*reflection* (flipping over)
*rotation* (turning)

can now be reinforced and combined using block or potato prints.

*Worksheet 6.4* asks children to complete strip patterns by drawing in the missing shapes.

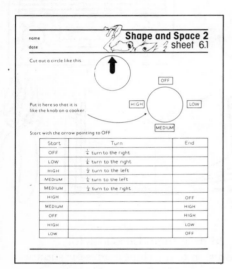

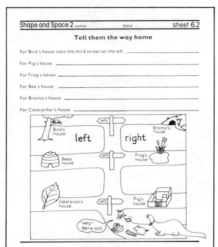

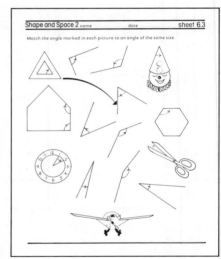

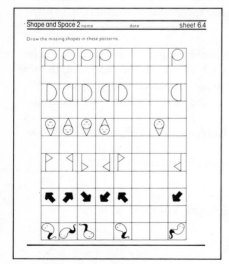

# References and resources

Ingleby, T. and Taylor, J. *Shapes* (six books), Longman Group UK Ltd 1969

Nuffield Mathematics Teaching Project, *Beginnings* ▽, *Environmental Geometry, Shape and Size* ▽, Nuffield Guides, Chambers/Murray 1967 (See Introduction page vii)

Shuard, H. and Williams, E. M. *Primary Mathematics Today*, Longman Group UK Ltd 1976

Walter, M. *Mirror Books* (Supplied with metal mirrors), Andre Deutsch

Cochranes of Oxford, *Orbit Materials*

Copyprint, *Copyprint Grids*

E. J. Arnold, *Tracing Shapes, Clixi, Polydron, Poleidoblocs* (Margaret Lowenfeld)

Longman Group UK Ltd, *Altair Design Pads 1 and 2*

Osmiroid, *Centicube Baseboard and Centicubes, Geoshape Stencils, Mirrors* (unbreakable plastic)

Philip & Tacey Ltd, *3-D Geometry Rubber Stamps, Mammoth Table* and *Floor Tiles, Plane Geometry Rubber Stamps, Symmetry* and *Reversal Pairing Cards*

Taskmaster, *Multi-purpose Mosaic Shapes, Wooden Cones, Cylinders* and *Spheres*

Burke, P., *Left, right*, Bronto Books Set B, *Animal Shapes*, Set C, Burke, P. and Albany, E. *Mini's log cabin*, Set E, Nuffield Maths 5–11, Longman Group UK Ltd, 1979.

Woodman, A. and Albany, E., *Mathematics Through Art and Design*, Unwin Hyman, 1988.

James Galt & Co. Ltd, *Pattern Printing Set*

Dime Project *Rotogram* (Packets of 10)

S.S.C.I.E. (Education Development Centre, Gorway Road, Walsall.) *Floor/Screen Turtle Resource Pack, Screen Turtle*

# Appendix

These diagrams are to help teachers overcome the problem of depicting three-dimensional figures on paper.
They are *not* intended as exercises for young children.

---

**Cube**—a prism with six square faces all of the same size.

1 Draw one square face.

2 Draw another square, slightly smaller, to one side and higher.

3 Join up corresponding corners to make a 'glass' cube.

4 Erase unwanted lines and shade to give a 'solid' appearance.

---

**Cuboid**—a prism with six rectangular faces, opposite faces being of the same shape and size. (Sometimes called a rectangular prism.)

 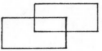 

1    2    3    4

---

**Triangular prism**—a solid with equal, parallel triangular ends of the same shape and rectangular lateral faces.

 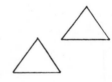 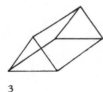 

2    3    4

---

**Prism**—a solid with parallel ends of the same shape and size, and rectangular lateral faces.

Example: Square prism

1    2    3    4

---

Example: Hexagonal prism

 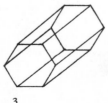 

1    2    3    4

---

**Cylinder**—a solid with a circular face and two equal, parallel circular ends. A cylinder could be thought of as a circular prism.

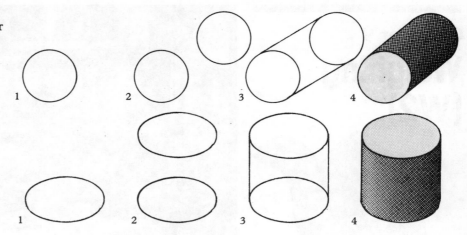

**Pyramid**—a solid with a straight-edged base and sloping triangular faces meeting a point (the apex).

Example: A square pyramid

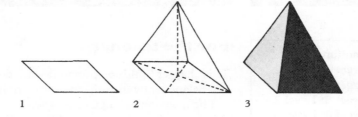

**Cone**—a solid with a flat circular base and a curved surface coming to a point (the apex). A cone could be thought of as a circular pyramid.

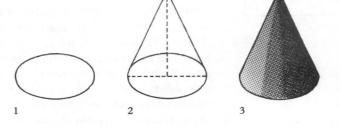

**Sphere**—a solid with a surface on which every point is the same distance from the centre of the solid.

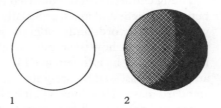

# Chapter 9
# Weighing (W2)

National Curriculum
Attainment Target 2: Level 2
Attainment Target 2: Level 4
Attainment Target 8: Level 2
Attainment Target 8: Level 3
Attainment Target 13: Level 2
Attainment Target 13: Level 3

## For the teacher

This chapter builds on previous work done on 'heavier than', 'lighter than' and balancing by introducing standard units for comparison.

The question of language—whether we should refer to the 'weight' or the 'mass' of an object—was discussed in Weighing 1, Chapter 9 of *Nuffield Maths 1 Teachers' Handbook*. The relevant section is reproduced here:

'In the strictly scientific sense, we can differentiate between weight and mass because weight is a *force*—the gravitational pull exerted on an object; whereas mass is the amount of matter in an object. Children may have seen the examples of weightlessness when watching television programmes about space travel. Although the astronauts are weightless, they still have mass. The *weight* or 'downward force' of an object can change, depending on where the measurement is made. The *mass* of an object remains the same no matter where the measurement is made.

Young children will be confused by any attempt to differentiate between weight and mass, especially as they live in an environment where certain words and modes of speech are firmly entrenched. Packages often show their 'nett weight'. If Dad has a 'weight problem' he does not say he is 'overmass'! It is generally accepted that the mass of an object is assessed by 'weighing' it on a balance against a known standard mass. (How long will it be before a kilogram weight becomes generally known as a kilogram mass?)

At this stage, what the children are experiencing by holding, lifting and balancing objects is *weight*.'

Before introducing standard units, the teacher may wish to know if a child has established the notion of weight and its invariance.

*Check-up on the invariance of weight*  For this check-up plasticine and a pair of balance scales are required.

Ask the child to make two balls of plasticine which weigh the same. If he has attempted this by using sight and muscle pull only, then ask him to put the balls of plasticine on the balance scales. If the balls do not balance, ask him if he can make them balance.

At an early stage he will not be able to see that by taking a little from one ball he might make them balance. Do not proceed further with this child. He needs a great deal more practical experience with materials.

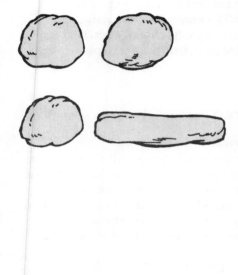

If the child is able to make the necessary adjustments to ensure that the two balls of plasticine make the scales balance, put the scales to one side and concentrate on the plasticine balls. Ask the child to roll one of the balls into a sausage. Then ask 'Which is heavier, the ball or the sausage?'

The answers given by the child will give clear clues to his thinking. He might say that there was more plasticine in the sausage so it must be heavier. He might say that they still weighed the same, but there was now more plasticine in the sausage. (See check-up on invariance of quantity and volume in Chapter 12, Capacity 2.) There will be all kinds of variation in response.

If the child is certain that the amount of plasticine has not changed, nothing has been added, nothing removed, and that as the pieces weighed the same originally so they must weigh the same now, then he is at a mature level of thinking.

However, it might be profitable to proceed further on a subsequent occasion. Begin again with the two balls of plasticine. Determine and accept that they weigh the same. Then break one ball of plasticine up into smaller pieces.

Similar questions will provoke another wide variety of response and will indicate the child's level of thinking at the time. Whatever his response it is probable that when the small pieces of plasticine are rolled back into one ball the child will be sure that we have returned to our starting point.

It must be emphasized that this kind of understanding cannot be achieved through teaching. Children may need a lot of varied experience with many kinds of materials before they can arrive, with certainty, at this notion of invariance.

## Summary of the stages

**W2**: 1  Introduction of the kilogram and $\frac{1}{2}$ kilogram

**W2**: 2  Using the kilogram and $\frac{1}{2}$ kilogram

**W2**: 3  Introduction of the 100 gram weight

## Vocabulary

Weight, heavy, light, heavier than, lighter than, weighs more than/less than, about the same as, balance, scales, kilogram, gram, 100 grams ('hecto'), $\frac{1}{2}$ kilo (500 grams), just over, just under.

## Equipment and apparatus

Balances and scales. Materials for weighing—plasticine or clay, marbles, pebbles, bottle-tops, sand, nails, stones, etc. Tins of lead, nuts and bolts, etc. which are heavier than 1 kilogram but small enough to be placed on scales, 1 kilogram packet of sugar, apples, oranges, bananas, large and small potatoes, teaspoons, desertspoons, egg-cups, mugs, cups, beakers, plastic tubs and cartons. Sawdust, dried peas, lentils, sweets, packets of crisps, conkers, pencils, crayons, etc.

## Working with the children

### W2 : 1   Introduction of the kilogram and ½ kilogram

There are not many objects usually found in a classroom which are heavier than a kilogram (1000 grams) but small enough to be put on the scale pan of a balance. The teacher is advised to prepare a collection of suitable objects—tins of lead shot, nuts and bolts, pebbles or sand, bags of marbles, bricks or rocks. (It is probably safer to use the word 'rock' rather than 'stone' just in case the children have heard of the stone used as a standard measure in the Imperial System.)

In activities suggested earlier in (Weighing 1, Chapter 9 of *Nuffield Maths 1 Teachers' Handbook*), objects were sorted heavier than, lighter than, or 'weigh about the same as' a book, should be repeated but this time using a kilogram weight as the standard of comparison.

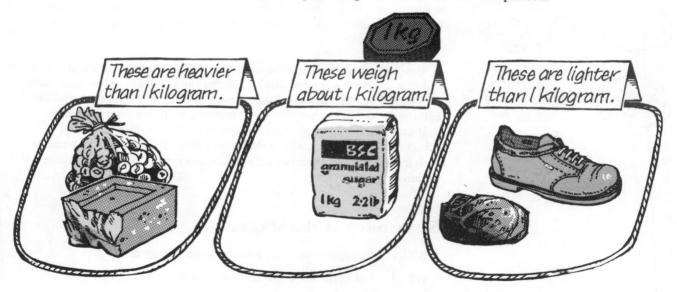

This sorting should be done by 'feel' or estimation and then checked by using balances.

The use of the phrase 'about 1 kilogram' should serve as a reminder that no measurement can be exact—it depends on the scales, whether they are level, how accurate the kilogram weight is made, etc. In order to save time when recording, the children should also be taught the abbreviation kg which stands for kilogram or kilograms, is written in lower case letters (no capitals) and without a full stop—unless it comes at the end of a sentence. The abbreviation for gram(s) is g.

When introducing the ½ kilogram the children must be given the opportunity to balance two ½ kilogram weights against one kilogram. They should also be reminded that the symbol ½ means:

$$\frac{1}{2}$$
← 1 kilogram
divided into
← 2 *equal* parts

The relationship between 1 kg and ½ kg can be further emphasized by allowing children to:

1  weigh out 1 kg of sand, pebbles or plasticine,

2  divide the material into two halves which balance each other,

3  finally, check that each half balances the ½ kg weight.

Many ½ kilogram weights are marked '500 grams' but at this stage this should be looked upon as another name for a ½ kilogram.

A similar activity to that used for the kilogram will allow the children to become familiar with the 'feel' of the ½ kilogram.

Some children may be able to sort like this:

| lighter than ½ kg | heavier than ½ kg but lighter than 1 kg | heavier than 1 kg |

The worksheets for this stage contain more written instructions than usual so teachers may have to help some children with reading difficulties.

*Worksheets should not be introduced until children have had plenty of
practical experience and opportunity for discussion.*

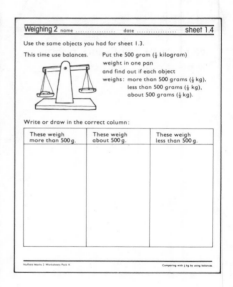

## W2: 2   Using the kilogram and ½ kilogram

At this stage kitchen scales or some other 'weighing machine' might be
introduced as an alternative to the simple balance. The children must be
given time to become familiar with the new apparatus and how to read the
dial, perhaps by checking weighings already done on the balance.

In this case, the weight of an object is assessed by the effect its downward
force has on a spring.

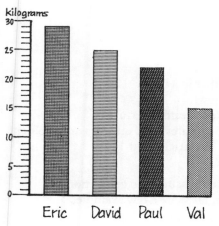

Children need as much experience as possible in weighing out 1 kilogram or ½ kilogram of different substances. A useful display can be made of a kilogram of sand, sugar, marbles, rice, lead shot, metal washers, etc., each on its own plate or shallow dish.

With practice it is possible to get quite close to the required amount when weighing substances like sand or rice; but it is more difficult when dealing with potatoes, apples or oranges, etc. The greengrocer often says, 'That's a bit over' or asks, 'Do you want just over or just under?' when serving a customer. Children may have heard their parents mention that they get 'about four apples to the pound'. (During the transition from imperial to metric measures, the ½ kilogram has the advantage of being quite close to the pound.)

Children should be given the chance to act as the shopkeeper and weigh out 1 kilogram or ½ kilogram of potatoes, carrots, turnips, onions, apples, oranges, etc., so that they learn approximately how many of each weigh 1 kg or ½ kg. As potatoes vary so much in size, it is a good idea to let the children sort them into 'large' and 'small' before weighing and counting.

When the children count the number of mugfuls or cupfuls of substance required to balance a kilogram or 500 gram weight, it is important to stress:

1 the container must be filled just to the brim—i.e. a 'level' cupful,
2 the substance is carefully tipped into the scale pan—we do not wish to weigh the container as well.

The fact that 1 litre of water weighs 1 kilogram (mentioned in Chapter 12, Capacity 2) gives an interesting link between capacity and weight.

Children are usually very interested to know how much they weigh in kilograms so if bathroom or other suitable scales are available, a graph might be drawn.

*Worksheets should not be introduced until children have had plenty of practical experience and opportunity for discussion.*

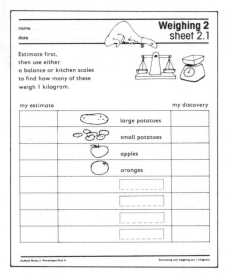

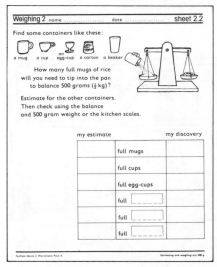

### W2: 3   Introduction of the 100 gram weight
As the kilogram (1000 grams) is rather a large unit for young children and

the gram is too small, the 100 gram weight may be considered more convenient for everyday weighing activities. Sweets, for example, are often sold in 100 gram packets and a greater variety of objects such as pencils, rubbers, rulers, crayons, conkers, beads, marbles, etc. can be balanced against the 100 gram weight to give results within the counting range of young children.

The Mathematical Association's Further Report on Primary Mathematics suggests that a 'homely' name is required for the 100 gram weight. *Primary Maths Today* by E. M. Williams and Shuard, Longman Group UK Ltd, suggests, '...children could call it a hecto, short for hectogram, its metric name which is not used in the International Standard but is available for informal usage.' Children do not have to be completely familiar with numbers up to 100 in order to use the 100 gram unit. They will look upon '100 grams' or 'hecto' as the name of a particular piece of metal.

The obvious uses of weighing are in shopping and cooking. Extra opportunities for weighing out required amounts occur if the class shop sells goods by weight rather than as separate items. A standard egg weighs approximately 50 grams, so the recipe given in Chapter 9 of *Nuffield Maths 1 Teacher's Handbook* can be repeated, but this time the required amounts can be weighed using standard measures.

*Recipe for 12 small cakes*

2 eggs
100 grams of margarine
100 grams of sugar
100 grams of flour

Cream the margarine and sugar together in a bowl.
Add 2 eggs and beat together in the bowl.
Add the flour and a little milk to make a creamy mixture.
Put in small cake tins and bake for 15 minutes to 20 minutes until golden in a moderately hot oven (Gas No. 5. Electricity 380°F).

There are many other recipes for cakes, biscuits and confectionary, which do not require the use of an oven. Here are a few examples:

*No-bake fruit bars*

Ingredients:
200 g digestive biscuits
50 g butter or margarine
50 g golden syrup
grated rind of 1 orange
100 g seedless raisins
50 g finely chopped mixed peel
little glacé icing

Method:
Roll the biscuits into fine crumbs. Melt butter and syrup and pour over the crumbs, and mix well until they are absorbed. Add orange rind, raisins and peel, and press into a 20 cm square tin which has been greased. Press firmly down and leave overnight to set. When firm, cut into finger-size bars or squares and top with glacé icing.

*Coconut ice*

Ingredients:
150 g desiccated coconut
4 tablespoonfuls condensed milk
300 g icing sugar
a drop of cochineal

Method:
Mix together the condensed milk and icing sugar. Stir in the coconut (the mixture should be very stiff) and divide into two parts. Tint one half of the mixture pale pink with cochineal. Shape the mixture into two 'identical' bars and press firmly together. Dust a plate or tin with icing sugar and leave coconut ice on this until firm.

*Magic fondants*

Ingredients:
200 g icing sugar
4 tablespoonfuls condensed milk

Method:
Sift icing sugar and blend in condensed milk until smooth and creamy. Flavour with peppermint, vanilla, fruit flavourings or coffee. Add suitable vegetable colourings. The mixture could be shared as evenly as possible among two or three children. They might make different shaped sweets and compare the numbers produced.

*Chocolate truffles*

Ingredients:
50 g butter
3 heaped dessertspoonfuls sweetened chocolate powder
1 heaped dessertspoonful icing sugar

Method:
Mix together and roll into balls on a plate sprinkled with chocolate powder.

If the only recipes available give the amounts in ounces, the teacher should convert these into metric measures. One ounce is just a shade over 28 grams but a simple and reasonably accurate conversion can be based on 25 grams for 1 ounce, 50 grams for 2 ounces, 100 grams for 4 ounces, etc.

*Weighing a parcel* Compared with weighing out a required amount, finding the weight of a parcel is much more difficult since it may involve considerable manipulation of standard weights or the accurate reading of a calibrated scale. However, previous experience of ordering can be used to find that a parcel weighs, for example, 'between 300 grams and 400 grams'. The package is heavier than 300 grams—but lighter than 400 grams.

113

Some children may be ready to weigh very light objects using 50 gram, 20 gram, 10 gram weights. There should be no attempt to impose a 'table of weight' on the children although some may discover such relationships as '5 hectos balance a ½-kilogram' for themselves.

In order to check if children are able to match, discriminate between and order weights, the following 'mystery parcel' activities are useful:

1  Make a set of five parcels which look identical but which weigh 1 kilogram, 700 grams, 500 grams, 200 grams and 100 grams respectively. Mark each parcel to show its weight. Make a similar unmarked set. Ask the child to pair the parcels according to their weight.

2  Take away the marked set. Mix up the unmarked set. Ask the child to put them in order of weight, starting with the heaviest.

3  Mix them up again. Add two more parcels which look the same as the others, one of which weighs more than 1 kilogram and one which weighs less than 100 grams. Ask the child to pick out the parcel which weighs 1 kilogram, the one which weighs 500 grams and the one which weighs 100 grams.

At this stage, the aim is for children to use and become familiar with the kilogram, ½ kilogram and 100 gram weights as standards against which everyday objects or materials are balanced. More accurate measurement is not appropriate for most children until later.

*Worksheets should not be introduced until children have had plenty of practical experience and opportunity for discussion.*

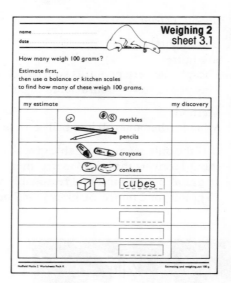

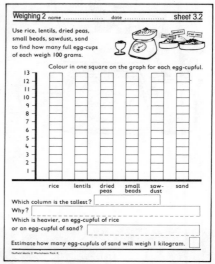

# References and Resources

Chaplin, S., *Bakery* (Teaching 5 to 13 Projects), Macdonald

Nuffield Mathematics Teaching Project, *Beginnings* ▽, Nuffield Guide, Chambers/Murray 1967 (See Introduction page vii)

Shuard, H. and Williams, E. M., *Primary Mathematics Today*, Longman Group UK Ltd 1976

Williams, M. E., *Come and Measure—Mass*, Macmillan 1975

E. J. Arnold, *Adjusted Metric Weights, Bucket Balance, Cylindrical Weights, Compression Scale (10 kg), Flat Pan Scale (5 kg), Plastic Simple Balance, Simple Balance*

Nicolas Burdett Ltd, *Analysis of a Kilogram, Bucket Balance, Compression Scales (10 kg), Equal Pan Balance, Personal Scales, Weighing Set*

Osmiroid, *Super Beamer Balance*

Philip & Tacey, Ltd, *Set of Iron Masses : Lead Adjusted*

Taskmaster Aids, *Circular Steel Weights, Hexagonal Iron Weights, Personal Scales, Stowaway Scales*

# Chapter 10
# Time (T2)

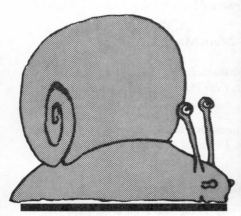

National Curriculum
Attainment Target 2: Level 2
Attainment Target 2: Level 4
Attainment Target 8: Level 2
Attainment Target 13: Level 2
Attainment Target 13: Level 3

## For the teacher

The previous chapter on Time (Chapter 10 in *Nuffield Maths 1 Teachers' Handbook*) emphasised that a child needs:

1 to relate time words to the actual passage of time,
2 to acquire some idea of the continuity of time.

Whilst continuing to reinforce and extend these ideas, the chapter will introduce the measurement of time by non-mechanical means and then deal with the stages gradually leading from reading a dial to telling the time using five minute intervals.

## Summary of the stages

**T2**: 1   Ways of measuring time

**T2**: 2   Reading a dial

**T2**: 3   Telling the time (hours, halves and quarters)

**T2**: 4   Telling the time (five-minute intervals)

**T2**: 5   Simple calculations involving time

**T2**: 6   Other units of time

## Vocabulary

Shadow, timer, water level, days of the week, o'clock, half past, quarter past, quarter to, minute hand (long), hour hand (short), minutes past, minutes to, fast, slow, months of the year.

## Equipment and apparatus

Real clocks of all kinds (working and broken), card for home-made clock face, brass paper fasteners, press-studs, paper circles for folding, large card or wooden clock faces, jigsaw clocks, candles, sand-timers, kitchen pinger, calendars of various types, copies of Radio Times and T.V. Times.

Instructions for making large display clock faces are in an appendix at the end of this chapter.

## Working with the children

### T2 : 1   Ways of measuring time

Making some of the following 'non-mechanical clocks' will provide practical experience illustrating the development of clocks and the need for more accurate ways of measuring time. It is suggested that these should be teacher-led activities. Once made, they can be used to reinforce the idea of the passage of time. They could even be used to *save* time! For example, 'Let's see if everything can be tidied away before the sand in the two-minute timer runs out.' Or, when changing for P.E., set the children off to 'Beat the drip' by asking, 'How many marks on the water clock will be covered before everyone is ready?'

*A sand timer*  Use two small empty bottles, one with a screw-on cap. Make a small hole in the cap. Put fine, dry sand into one bottle, screw on the cap and tape the necks of the bottles together to make an 'egg-timer'. Adjust the amount of sand to make the timer measure a whole number of minutes.

*A water clock*  Use a clean, empty tin. (A soup tin will do.) Make a very small hole in the bottom of the tin. Place the tin on top of a tall jar which has vertical sides. Fill the tin with water. Every minute mark the water level in the jar on a strip of gummed paper.

*The shadow stick*  Outside, on a sunny day, push a stick vertically into the ground. At 10 o'clock mark where the end of its shadow is. Measure the length of the shadow. Mark and measure again at hourly intervals. Ask the children to make a chart like this:
at 10 o'clock the shadow was ___ cm long.
at 11 o'clock the shadow was ___ cm long.
etc.
The children may notice something else about the shadow.

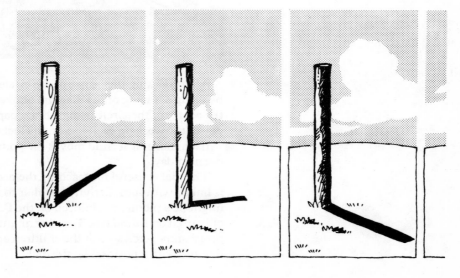

*A pin timer* Use a ruler and pin to make small marks half a centimetre apart on the side of a candle. Stick a pin in each mark. Fix the candle and use it to measure time by counting how many pins drop out. Time can now be measured in 'pin units'.

*A candle clock* Use candles of the same size and thickness. Fix one firmly into a tin lid, light the candle and every half hour mark its height on an unlit candle. Use the marked candle to calibrate other candles in half-hour intervals.

*There are no worksheets published for this stage.*

### T2 : 2   Reading a dial

Children can be introduced to dial-reading through a simple 'days of the week' dial. A circle with a radius of about 15 cm is drawn in the centre of a piece of card, leaving enough room for pictures to be pasted around the circle.

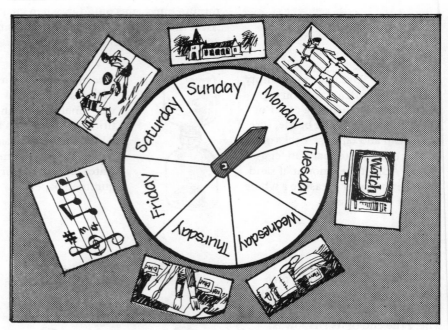

After marking the centre of the circle, it can be divided into seven parts by using a tracing of the diagram above. A stiff cardboard pointer is fixed at the centre of the circle using a brass paper fastener or press stud. Write a day of the week on each sector, in clockwise order, round the circle.

Each morning a child moves the pointer in a clockwise direction on to the next day.

The dial is useful for teaching the order of the days, especially if each day is linked with some activity peculiar to it. For example, next to Monday might be a picture of children on the P.E. climbing apparatus because it is only used on Mondays; Tuesday might be the day for a special television programme, etc., so that the children are matching a particular event with a day and with a position on the dial.

*Matching events with the clock face* To begin with, early activities in clock-reading will be merely informal references made by the teacher to the class linking a routine situation to a particular time on the school clock. 'When the little hand is on 10 and the big hand reaches the 12, it will be ten o'clock and time for us to drink our milk.' The times of favourite television programmes, meal times, and bed times are often recognised on the clock dial by children before they come to school. Much simple discussion with incidental references to the clock face and time should be going on long before children begin to draw clock faces or write in the times.

Often young children confuse the minute hand with the hour hand. To overcome this they should have access to play clocks—of all kinds. In the first instance, it is helpful if the hands are different in size, shape and colour.

There are many clocks of this sort on the market. Some are similar to a jigsaw with self-correcting pieces for numerals and picture panels illustrating the activities of a child during the course of a normal day. Others have removable numerals and the child must know the order of numbers from one to twelve in order to fit them correctly. Both kinds help the child to establish the layout of the clock face and realise that one hand is larger than the other.

A home-made clock face can also be used to establish the positions of the numerals.

Draw a good sized circle in felt tip on a piece of card (suggested diameter of 30 cm). Mark in the centre point and the four points in the north, south, east and west positions. Cover with clear *Contact* and punch two holes through the top of the card so that it may be hung by string threaded through the holes.

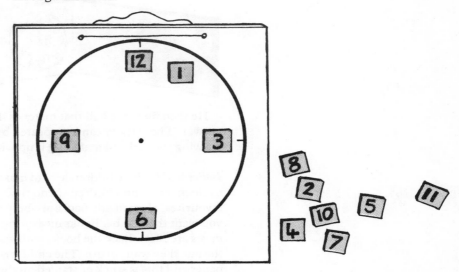

Cut out 12 round or rectangular pieces of card. Write on each card a digit from one to twelve. Stick a curl of Sellotape on the back of each. The small numbered shapes will now adhere to the surface and can be removed easily. Children can practise placing the numerals in the correct positions. Further small cards can be made should any be lost or damaged.

Make the long hand and short hand using a different shape and colour for each.

Place the long hand on top of the short hand and push a paper fastener through both. Now push the paper fastener through the centre point marked on the circle and fix the clip in position at the back of the clock face.

Children will find it easier to place the digits correctly if they position the 12, 6, 9 and 3 first. These four positions were marked out earlier and once they are fixed, children find little difficulty in placing the rest. The hands can then be moved into any position whilst the child 'talks time' to his teacher or a friend.

*Self-corrective jig saws*  These can be made by the teacher. Each set consists of two parts which fit together exactly and will not fit any other part. On one part a clock face is stamped showing the time (the hours only to begin with). The opposite part should illustrate the activity that might be going on at that particular time.
For example:

     9 o'clock  :  school time.
    11 o'clock  :  play time.
    12 o'clock  :  dinner time.
     3 o'clock  :  story time.

There are many variations of this activity. For instance, when children are beginning to read they could match a clock dial to the correct written time.

Later these may be used for testing the child's understanding. The child is given the parts showing the clock faces. He chooses one, copies it into his workbook and writes the time underneath.

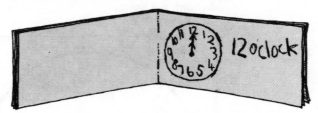

He then finds the half that matches the one he copied and checks his answer. The activity can be repeated by using the written part first, drawing the dial and matching it up with the correct card.

*Individual books*  Children love to make their own books and those relating to clocks and how children spend their day seem to be among the favourites. Homemade books are best, since these can be as thick or thin as you want them to be. Books measuring 20 cm × 15 cm with 4 to 5 double pages are ideal. Back the books with wallpaper and let the children choose the one they want to use. The child writes the title on a separate strip of paper and this is stuck or stapled on the cover.

*List of titles*
What I did yesterday.    What I did last night.    What I do on Saturdays.
What I do on Sundays.    What I do after school.    What I do at school.

The book is opened at the first double page. Children use the clock stamp on one side to record a special time and draw a picture or write about what they were doing at that time on the other page.

*Worksheets should not be introduced*
*until children have had plenty of*
*practical experience*
*and opportunity for discussion.*

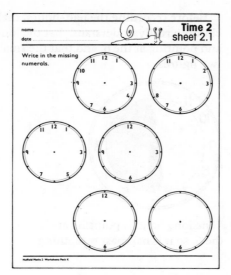

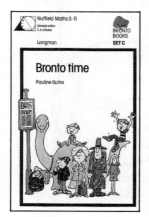

### T2: 3    Telling the time (hours, halves and quarters)

Once a child is familiar with the layout of a clock-face and has had some experience of associating particular events with the position of the hands, a more systematic approach to telling the time can be adopted. Even children who have learned to tell the time at home are not always sure of the time when the hour hand is pointing somewhere between two figures on the clock-face. For example, they often read 4.30 as 'half past five'.

The teacher should first make sure that the child can read the hours ('When the long hand is on the twelve, the time is something o'clock.').

One hand is missing but the time is recorded beneath the clock, the child draws in the missing hand.

The time is recorded on the clock face. The child records it in writing beneath the clock.

The time is written beneath the clock. The child puts the hands in the correct place.

Before recording the half-hours, the teacher should check that the children really understand that the long hand is half-way round the face and pointing at the 6, and that the small hand is pointing halfway between two figures.

'The long hand is pointing at the 6, so it is half past something.'

'The small hand is half-way between the 4 and the 5, so it is half past 4.'

Old clocks whose hands still move correctly, even if the mechanism is broken, are very useful to illustrate the relative movements of the two hands.

 *In one hour:*

the long hand moves all the way round the clock . . .

. . . but the small hand only moves from one figure to the next.

Another way to help the children appreciate the movement of both hands is to draw a clock face with only the hour hand on it.

This is a picture of a clock which is still working but the minute hand has dropped off. Can you guess the time? (Worksheet T2: 3.4)

The gradual movement of the hour-hand will also be emphasized by making a 'Bedtime chart'. The teacher draws up a chart to show bedtimes in half-hour intervals. The hands on the clock-faces can be put in by the children. Each child in the class or in a group is given a coloured star to stick in the column showing when he or she went to bed.

| 7 o'clock | half past 7 | 8 o'clock | half past 8 | 9 o'clock | half past 9 |

When the graph is complete the children use it to answer such questions as:

How many children went to bed at 8 o'clock?
How many children went to bed after half past 8?

Once the teacher has reminded the children there are four quarters in a whole one, by folding a circle, 'quarter past' and 'quarter to' can be dealt with. Again it is important to draw attention to the positions of *both* hands.

Quarter past

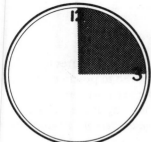

Quarter to

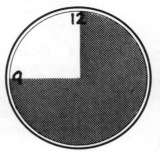

'When the long hand
points to the 3,
it is *quarter past*
something.'

'The small hand
is just past the 7
so it is *quarter past* 7.'

'When the long hand
points to the 9,
it is *quarter to*
something.'

'The small hand
has nearly reached the 4
so it is *quarter to* 4.'

*Worksheets should not be introduced until children have had plenty of practical experience and opportunity for discussion.*

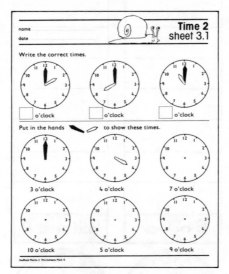

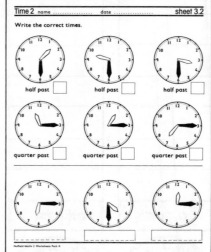

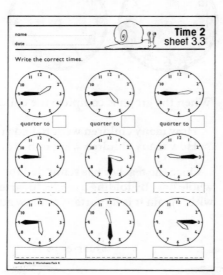

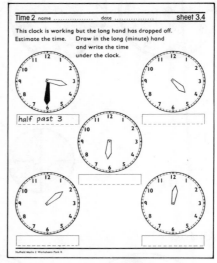

## T2 : 4  Telling the time (five minute intervals)

The emphasis at this stage is on the minute hand taking 60 minutes to travel once round the clock face so the children will need to practice counting in fives up to 60, and relating each multiple to a position on the clock face. The children need to realize that, when looking at the minute hand, the numerals on the clock face tell them *how many sets of five minutes*.

In the first instance, it is probably easier to concentrate on telling the time in five minute intervals using the form '10 minutes past' and 'twenty minutes to'. A special clock face divided into two halves of different colours with either a single minute hand or a single interleaving circle is the best way to illustrate this. (See instructions for making these in the Appendices to this chapter.)

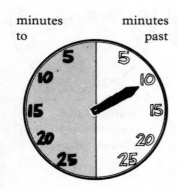

After some experience of reading and recording the time (still in five minute intervals) in the 'minutes past/minutes to' form, some children may be ready to go on to use the form in which time is expressed as hours and minutes without using the words 'past' or 'to'. For example, 7.20, 2.55 or ten thirty-five.

This is a good point at which to introduce the 'Sixty Game' in which the teacher gives a multiple of five (less than 60) and asks for the number which 'makes it up to 60'. For example, (20, *40*) (45, *15*) (25, *35*), etc. This will help the children to connect *20 minutes to* 8, for example, with *40 minutes past* 7 or 7.40.

One particular problem arises with five minutes past which should be written as, for example, 6.05. The zero indicates that there are no tens of minutes. It is important that this is taught before the children attempt Worksheets T2: 4.5 and T2: 4.6.

*Worksheets should not be introduced until children have had plenty of practical experience and opportunity for discussion.*

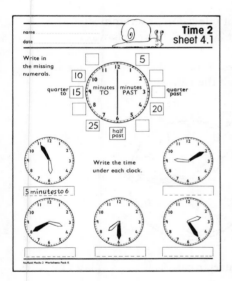

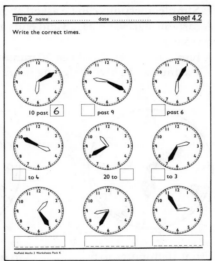

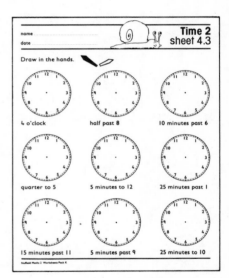

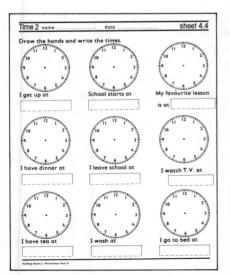

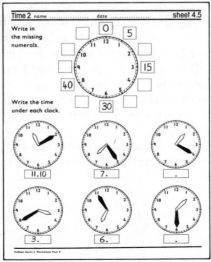

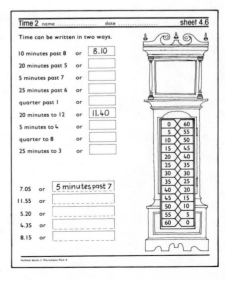

## T2: 5 Simple calculations involving time

By using a clock face with a movable minute hand, calculating the interval of time between two numbered positions is just like counting on in fives around a circular number line.

For example:

from                                    to

20 minutes

Simple questions can be asked about television programmes:
A cartoon starts at 5 past 3 and ends at 20 past 3. How long was the cartoon?
A film starts at 4.15 and last 20 minutes. What is the time when it ends?
Examples can involve 'going through the 12'.

From 10 minutes to 6          to quarter past 6          is 25 minutes.

At this stage, calculations should be restricted to multiples of 5 minutes.

Some children may be able to tackle problems involving hours and minutes. For example, 'How long is it from 10 past 3 until 20 past 5?'

This will lead to playing the 'Two clocks game'. Mary and Jane each have a clock face. Each sets her own clock face at the time of her choice. Mary works out the interval between her time and Jane's; Jane works out the interval between hers and Mary's. The two intervals should add up to 12 hours.

It is not recommended at this stage that children attempt formal computations involving hours and minutes.

*Worksheets should not be introduced until children have had plenty of practical experience and opportunity for discussion.*

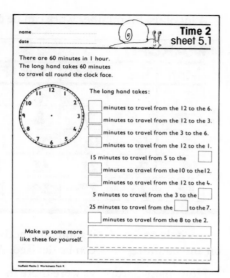

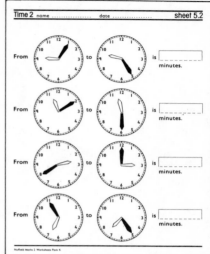

### T2: 6  Other units of time

The importance of the number 60 in time measure should again be emphasised and related to number work.

> There are 60 seconds in 1 minute.
> There are 60 minutes in 1 hour.
> Half an hour is 30 minutes.
> Half a minute is 30 seconds, etc.

As a nice calming activity, get all the children to close their eyes and ask them to estimate when a minute has passed from a given starting signal. As each child thinks the minute has passed he opens his eyes and puts up his hand. There will probably be a very wide range in the estimates—especially if one or two fall asleep!

Now teach them the 'elephant method' for estimating a minute. By mentally counting, 'One elephant, two elephants, three elephants . . .' up to . . . 'sixty elephants', a rhythm is set up which results in a surprisingly accurate estimate of a minute. A commercially produced 'seconds timer', a clock or watch with a seconds hand can be used as a check on the 'elephant method', to estimate any number of seconds.

A 'seconds pendulum' can be made by suspending a small weight on a string just under one metre long and allowing it to swing freely. The weight should not swing more than about 25 centimetres either side of the central position. A stop-watch or stop-clock fascinates most children. Many timing activities can be devised involving seconds—'How many towers of 5 bricks can you build in 20 seconds?' or 'How many beads can you thread in 30 seconds?' etc.

*Using the calendar*  Be sure the children know the names of days of the week and months of the year in correct order. Ask the children to find out on which day of the week they were born. Read the poem:

> 'Monday's child is full of woe,
> Tuesday's child has far to go . . .', etc.

The children collect all the information for the class and make a block graph of 'Monday's children, Tuesday's children' etc.

127

A lot of useful number work can be done using a page from a calendar.

| MARCH | | | | | | 1990 |
|------|------|------|------|------|------|------|
| Mon | Tue | Wed | Thur | Fri | Sat | Sun |
|  |  |  | 1 | 2 | 3 | 4 |
| 5 | 6 | 7 | 8 | 9 | 10 | 11 |
| 12 | 13 | 14 | 15 | 16 | 17 | 18 |
| 19 | 20 | 21 | 22 | 23 | 24 | 25 |
| 26 | 27 | 28 | 29 | 30 | 31 | |

A whole series of questions and activities involving counting, counting on and counting back can be devised. A few examples are:

How many Saturdays were there in March 1990?
Brownies meet on Wednesdays. How many meetings were there in March?
How many schooldays were there?
On which day do the shops close for half a day?
How many half-day closings were there in March?
Which day of the week was 1st April 1990?
If Susan's Grandfather gives her 5p every Saturday, how much was she given in March?

The children can play the 'x days' time game. Two children have a calendar and find 'today'. John says, 'In five days' time, I am going to the pictures.' David must give the day and date. Or David may say, 'Three days ago I played football.' John must give the day and date.

Remind the children that the five in the phrase 'in five days' time' does not include 'today'.

The 'Knuckle Method' for finding the number of days in a month interests children and many find it easier than remembering the 'Thirty days hath September' rhyme.

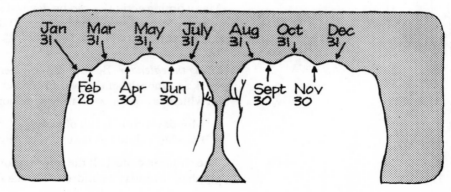

*Worksheets should not be introduced until children have had plenty of practical experience and opportunity for discussion.*

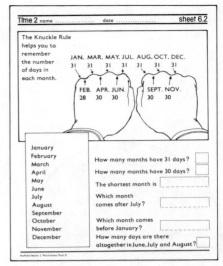

## References and resources

Burke, P., *Bronto time*, Bronto Books Set C, Nuffield Maths 5–11, Longman Group UK Ltd 1979

Matthews, G. and J., *Passage of Time*, Early Mathematical Experiences Project, Longman Group UK Ltd Third Edition 1990

Williams, M. E., *Come and Measure — Time*, Macmillan 1975

*Clocks*, Starters Series, Macdonald

*How Much Time?, Times Through the Day*, Strip Books, Philip & Tacey Ltd

*Time and Clocks*, First Library Series, Macdonald

E. J. Arnold, *Clock Faces, Rubber Stamp, Sand Glass Timer, Seconds Timer, Stop Watch, Sundial, Working Clock*

Osmiroid Ednl., *Rotascan Clock, Tocker Timers, Ivanson Timers, Water Timers*

Taskmaster Ltd., *Seconds Stop Clock, Ten Seconds Timer, Time Glasses* (10 min., 30 min.)

Philip & Tacey Ltd., *Clock Face Rubber Stamps*, 12-hour edition, 24-hour edition, *Numerex Blank Clock Face Rubber Stamps*

# Appendix 1

*A home-made clock face* In the absence of a large commercially produced clock face, teachers might wish to make their own. (Rubber stamp clock faces are not large enough for demonstration purposes.) It is worth taking a little care in making the first 'prototype' since this can be used as a template for any future versions you may wish to make.

On paper, draw a circle with a radius of at least 10 cm (i.e. 20 cm diameter). This can be done either by using compasses or by drawing round a circular plate. Cut out the circle and fold it into four. (This will find the centre if you have drawn round a plate, and will also show whether or not the plate was close to a true circle.) The folds mark out four positions on the clock face. The other positions may be marked either by using a protractor (angles of 30 degrees at the centre) or by further folding.

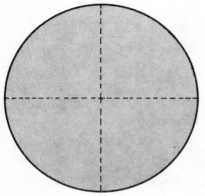

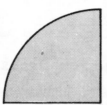

Fold to produce this.

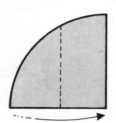

Fold along dotted line.

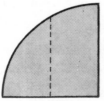

Open out to this.

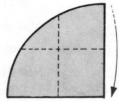
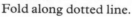

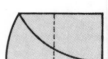

Fold along dotted line.

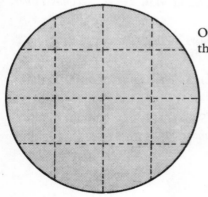

On opening out the paper, the creases appear like this.

Draw lines through the centre to join points where creases cross the circumference, thus dividing it into 12 equal parts.

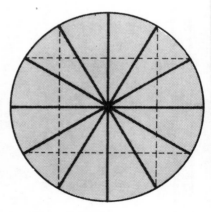

Use the template of the circle divided into 12 equal parts to mark out a clock face on stiff card. The 'hands' can either be cut from card and secured by a brass paper fastener, or can be made from coloured pipe cleaners poked through a small hole at the centre. Bend over at the back of the clock to prevent them slipping through.

Using the template, different versions of the clock face can be made. For example, the 'minutes past/minutes to' face mentioned in stage T2: 4.

# Appendix 2

*Clock face using interleaved circles*  Use the template to mark out a clock
face on stiff card as before. Cut a straight slit from the centre to the edge of
the circle at '12 o'clock'. (Alternatively, cut right to the edge of the card
with scissors and then Sellotape across the back just above the 12 mark.)

   Now cut out a smaller circle (about 8 cm radius) from card of a different
colour. Make a straight cut from the edge to the centre. Draw a 'hand'
along one edge of the cut and push the other edge through the slit in the
clock face.

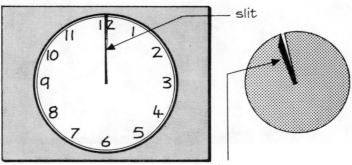

hand drawn on

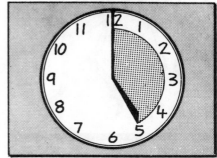

circles interleaved

To make the hour hand, cut out an even smaller circle of another colour
(radius 6 cm). Make a straight cut and draw in a 'hand' as before. Interleave
to make a clock with two hands.

   If the two circles are made of some clear material, such as overhead
projector transparencies, the whole of both hands will be visible.

   The interleaving circle idea is particularly useful when the children are
at the 'minutes past/minutes to' stage. In this case, the back and front of
the 'minute hand circle' are coloured to match the numerals of the two
halves of the clock face. The circle is slotted into the face one way for
'minutes past'; it is turned over and inserted the other way for 'minutes to'.

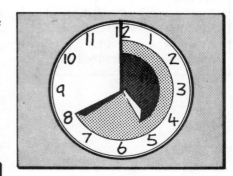

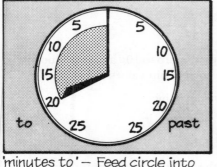

'minutes to' — Feed circle into
slot          this way.

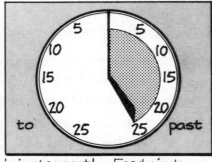

'minutes past' — Feed circle
into slot          this way.

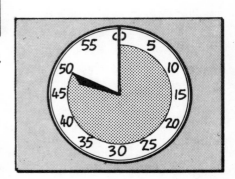

When the children reach the 'hours and minutes' form (i.e. 7.25, 8.55,
etc.), the circle can be slotted into a clock face marked 5, 10, 15, 20 ... 45,
50, 55.

   The advantage of the interleaving circle clock is the visual effect—the
angle 'swept out' by the hand (or to be 'swept out' in moving up to the 12
position) is clearly indicated.

# Chapter 11
# Money (M2)

National Curriculum
Attainment Target 3: Level 2
Attainment Target 5: Level 2
Attainment Target 8: Level 2
Attainment Target 13: Level 2

## For the teacher

There is a close connection between activities involving money and number work. The two should reinforce each other. Both are exact, as opposed to the measurement of length, weight, capacity, etc., which is approximate.

The aims of this chapter are:

1 to build on previous work (see Chapter 11, Money in *Nuffield Maths 1 Teachers' Handbook*),
2 to introduce the 20p and 50p coins,
3 to extend the range of activities using money.

## Summary of the stages

**M2**: 1   Reinforcement of coin recognition up to 10p and introduction of 20p and 50p coins. Ordering of coin values

**M2**: 2   Breakdown of coins—equivalent values

**M2**: 3   Making amounts of money up to 20p

**M2**: 4   Addition—simple shopping bills

**M2**: 5   Giving change and finding the difference by counting on

**M2**: 6   Subtracting by 'taking away'

## Vocabulary

Money, coin, value, penny, pence, shop, buy, sell, cost, change, bill, spend, amount, shopkeeper, bank, cash, cashier, die, dice, total, spinner.

# Equipment and apparatus

Cardboard, plastic or real coins; gummed paper money, dice, matching cards, inset boards, money dominoes, price cards.

# Working with the children

### M2: 1 Reinforcement of coin recognition and introduction of 50p coin

*Sorting activities using real coins:*

a) Sorting into two groups according to colour,

b) sorting according to value, 1p, 2p, 5p, 10p, 20p, 50p,

c) sorting with eyes closed—feeling shape, size, thickness and edges.

*Other activities to reinforce coin recognition*

a) Money Dominoes (described in Chapter 11 on Money in *Nuffield Maths 1 Teachers' Handbook*). A few more dominoes, similar to those described below, are added in order to bring in the 20p and 50p coins.

b) Inset Boards, with spaces the correct sizes for coins, and the value of the coin written in each space. The values 1p, 2p, 5p, 10p, 20p and 50p are marked on the sides of wooden cubes to make dice (or see page 131). After each throw of the dice, a player selects the appropriate coin and places it in the correct space. The winner is the first player with a full card.

c) Several commercially produced games are available (see References and Resources section at the end of this chapter).

d) Ordering coins according to value.

$$\text{is worth more than} \longrightarrow$$
$$50p \rightarrow 20p \rightarrow 10p \rightarrow 5p \rightarrow 2p \rightarrow 1p$$
$$\text{is worth less than} \longrightarrow$$
$$1p \rightarrow 2p \rightarrow \text{etc.}$$

*Worksheets should not be introduced until children have had plenty of practical experience and opportunity for discussion.*

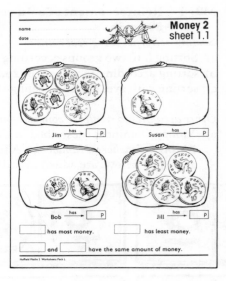

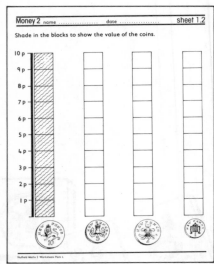

## M2: 2  Breakdown of coins—equivalent value

Some work has already been done on equivalent value of coins in *Teachers' Handbook 1*. This section aims to reinforce this work, extend it to include the 50p coin and to make use of a pattern approach. The development of patterns of coins is probably best attempted as a group or class activity, especially when a large number of possibilities arises. The children should be encouraged to look for a pattern and to use the idea of exchange to obtain new versions of the same monetary value.

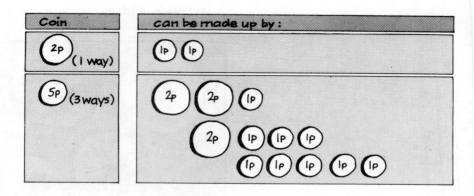

As an alternative, the child places coins to the value of 5p in each section of a base-board:

A similar approach for the 10p coin, using 5p, 2p and 1p coins, gives this pattern:

```
10     5  5
       5  2  2  1
       5     2  1  1  1
       5        1  1  1  1  1
    2  2  2  2  2
    2  2  2  2     1  1
    2  2  2        1  1  1  1
    2  2           1  1  1  1  1  1
    2              1  1  1  1  1  1  1  1
                   1  1  1  1  1  1  1  1  1  1
```

Using 10p, 5p, 2p and 1p coins, there are over 30 ways of making 20p and many more ways of making 50p. It is not really worthwhile to attempt them all but, by using the baseboard, children can find a selection of possibilities.

*Worksheets should not be introduced until children have had plenty of practical experience and opportunity for discussion.*

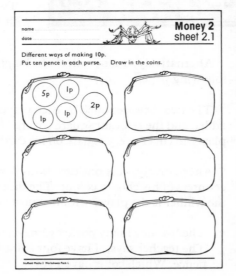

### M2 : 3    Making amounts of money up to 20p

a) Using the coins 1p, 2p, 5p, 10p, 20p, make sets of matching cards, using no more than four coins on a card.

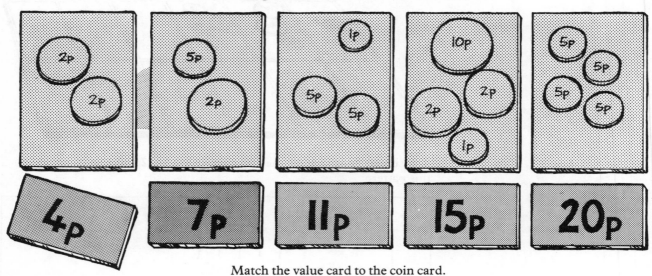

Match the value card to the coin card.

b) *The cash and cover game*
Each player has a base board and some counters:

| 0p | 1p | 2p | 3p | 4p | 5p |
|----|----|----|----|----|----|
| 6p | 7p | 10p | 11p | 12p | 15p |
| 20p | 21p | 22p | 25p | 30p | 40p |

Two dice are made from wooden cubes with faces marked 0p, 1p, 2p, 5p, 10p, 20p.

Alternatively, 'money dice' can be plaited using the diagram on the following page.

The two dice are rolled by each player in turn. The amounts shown are added and the relevant square covered by a counter. The winner is the first player to cover every square on his card.

Alternatively, only one card is used and each player is given a set of counters of his chosen colour. The dice are rolled as before but this time the winner is the player with the most counters on the full card.

c) The 'Money in my pocket game' is useful for those odd few minutes. The teacher says, 'I have four coins in my pocket, they add up to 12 pence. Which coins have I got?'

# THIS PAGE MAY BE PHOTOCOPIED WITHOUT PRIOR PERMISSION

Cut out carefully along all the _____ lines and mountain fold all the
------- lines, making sharp creases.

Start by plaiting the 0p face over a blank square, then continue by
plaiting 5p over blank, 20p over blank, 1p over blank, 10p over blank and
2p over blank.

The final move is to tuck the
tapered end under the 0p face.

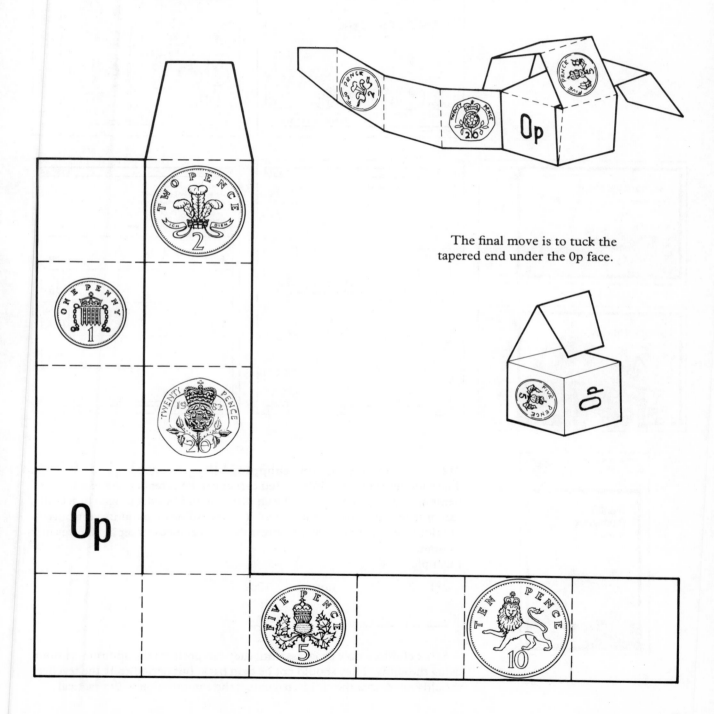

*Worksheets should not be introduced until children have had plenty of practical experience and opportunity for discussion.*

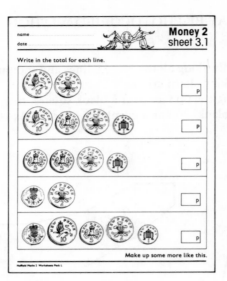

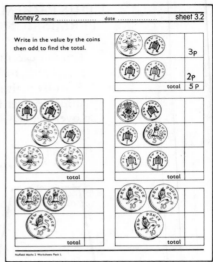

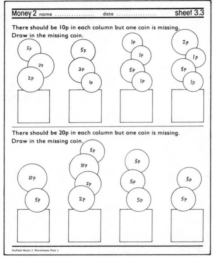

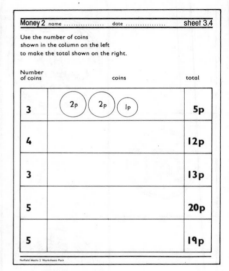

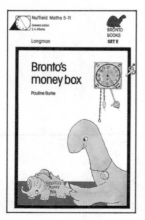

## M2: 4   Addition—simple shopping bills

The shopping activities introduced earlier can be extended to include more items and to use more coins. The children should be encouraged to set out real or token coins by each addition. The recording of amounts vertically provides a good opportunity to stress the importance of keeping figures in columns.

Example:

```
  1   2     p     not        12p
      4     p                  4p
+     2     p              +   2p
  _____               _____
```

Some children may progress until they can perform the addition without using the coins. They should not be held back, but periodically the teacher should ensure that the children connect the computation with practical situations. The slick manipulation of figures does not necessarily imply the full understanding of monetary value.

Although some of the addition problems on the worksheets use two-digit numbers of pence, no formal approach to regrouping is required at this stage. (That is, the so-called 'carry one' does not arise.) However, children should be encouraged to spot 'pairs that make 10' [1 + 9, 2 + 8, 6 + 4, etc.] even when adding three or four figures.

For example,

$$\begin{matrix} 7p \\ 8p \\ \underline{3p} \\ \underline{\phantom{xx}} \end{matrix}$$

'7 and 3 make 10; and 8 makes 18.'
is easier than
'7 and 8 make 15; and 3 makes 18.'

There are three main types of problems on the worksheets:

| 6 p<br>2 p<br><u>1 p</u> | 16p<br>20p<br><u>3p</u> | 6p<br>7p<br><u>+ 4p</u> |
|---|---|---|
| Total does not exceed 10p. | Columns may be added separately since no regrouping is involved (i.e. no 'carrying'). | Total does not exceed 20p and 'spotting tens' can be used. |

*Worksheets should not be introduced until children have had plenty of practical experience and opportunity for discussion.*

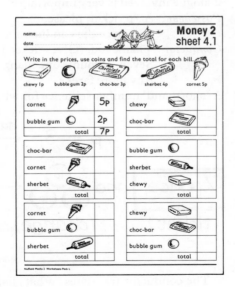

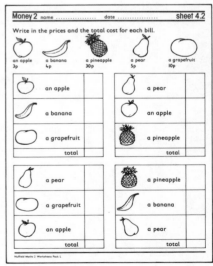

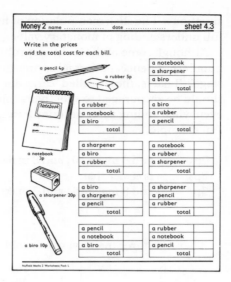

## M2 : 5    Giving change and finding the difference by counting on

In practical situations when change is given, the shopkeeper or bus conductor does not 'take away' to find the change required. He counts on to 'make up' the difference between the cost of the goods or ticket and the value of the coin(s) offered. This method is used countless times a day and yet, because no recorded answer is needed, often the shopkeeper/conductor is not aware of the amount of money given as change—he only knows it is right!

Children need to enact what happens when money is paid and change given, using clearly priced articles and either real or token money. The dialogue involved is very important:

*Passenger :*   A 7p ticket, please.

           (He gives the conductor a 10p coin.)

*Conductor :* Thank you. (Gives ticket.)

           Seven—(counts out change) eight, nine, ten.

           Any more fares?

A 'shorthand' number sentence for what has happened is:

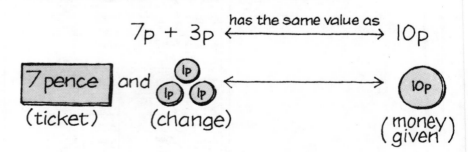

The conductor translates 'What change must I give if 10p is offered for a 7p ticket?' into 'Start at 7p and count on to 10p.' He is really solving the problem $7 + \square = 10$, but he does not have to 'fill in the box' because the passenger puts the 'answer' in his pocket!

A similar situation arises when comparing two amounts of money in order to find the difference in value. For example, 'Mary has 7p and John has 4p. How much more has Mary than John?' It is misleading to use the phrase 'take away' in this case since a child told to 'take John's 4p away from Mary's 7p' could well answer, 'But please Sir, Mary hasn't got John's 4p so how can I take it away?' Although the process involved is subtraction, it is the *comparative* aspect ('finding the difference') and not the physical removal aspect ('taking away') which is being used.

This example emphasises yet again the importance of language and warns against rushing into the use of symbolism (' − means take away') before the process is understood and described in words.

*Worksheets should not be introduced until children have had plenty of practical experience and opportunity for discussion.*

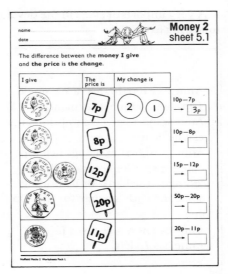

## M2: 6 Subtraction by 'taking away'

The physical removal aspect of subtraction arises in money transactions where the problem involves finding the amount left after some money has been spent, lost or given away.

Again, it is very important to connect the language used in describing these transactions with the arithmetical process. Children need to be familiar with such expressions as 'pay out', 'lose', 'give away', etc., in situations using real or token money before any attempt is made to use symbols. The stages of development, as before, are:

a) Perform the transaction using real or token money.
b) Talk about what happens,
c) Write about what happens, and finally,
d) Introduce the appropriate symbols as a 'shorthand' for the written version.

The children should first 'act out' the story or the 'John and Anne' display board could be used with the coins placed on the board.

Discussion follows with the teacher emphasising the key words:

'John has seven pence.
John gives three pence to Anne.
How much does John have left?
John has four pence left.'

141

The amount of actual writing is reduced by providing worksheets

John has [ p ]     John gives Anne [ p ]

How much does John have left? [ p ]

[ p ] take away [ p ] leaves [ p ]

Gradually, as the children become more confident in the use of the language describing the situation, the last line becomes:

7p − 3p → 4p

A very important stage in the development of subtraction arises in the following examples:

| | Anne | John |
|---|---|---|
| Anne has 10p (in this case a single 10p coin). John has no money. Anne wants to give 3p to John. How can he do it? Anne must first exchange her 10p coin for smaller coins—either by 'going to the bank' or by finding someone with 'change for the 10p coin.' Anne can now give 3p to John Anne has 7p left | | |

A similar situation arises if Anne has, say a 10p coin and a 5p coin and wants to give John 8p.

The children need plenty of experience of this type of practical problem.

The need to carry out an exchange before it is possible to 'take away', may well be the child's first introduction to what, much later, will be the basis of the so-called 'decomposition' method of subtraction.

Whilst stressing the importance of the chain:

actions → spoken words → writing → symbols,

we should not forget to reverse the process by asking children to create a situation or 'make up a story' to fit 15p − 6p → 9p

Here the chain is:

symbols → What do they say? → What do they mean? → Give an example.

In the case of subtraction, a number of quite different 'stories' can be made up to fit a statement such as:

10p − 7p → 3p

a)  I started with 10p, I lost 7p so I have 3p left.
b)  Susan has 10p, Lynne has 7p, so Susan has 3p more than Lynne. (Or Lynne has 3p less than Susan!)
c)  In order to make my money up to 10p from 7p, I shall need to add 3p.

a) Involves physical removal. Both b) and c) illustrate the comparative aspect of subtraction. In the case of c), the relationship between addition and subtraction is emphasized.

*Worksheets should not be introduced until children have had plenty of practical experience and opportunity for discussion.*

## References and resources

Dewhirst, W. *Bronto at the zoo*, *Bronto at the fair*, Set D, Burke, P. and Albany, A. *Bronto's money box*, Set E, Nuffield Maths 5–11, Longman Group UK Ltd 1979

Frobisher, B. and Gloyn, S., *Infants Learn Mathematics*, Ward Lock 1969

Nuffield Mathematics Teaching Project, Beginnings $\triangledown$, Nuffield Guide, Chambers/Murray 1976 (See Introduction page vii)

E. J. Arnold, *Cardboard Token Coins, Coin Recognition Cards, Coin Stamps, Decimal Money Dominoes, Dice with Coinage Values, Gummed Printed Coins, 'Mr. Money', 'New Penny Pocket Money', Plastic Token Coins, Shopping Set*

Galt, *'Banker', Cardboard and Plastic Coins, Coin Matching Dominoes, Decimal Coin Rubber Stamps, 'Fill a Purse', 'Shopping is Fun', Sorting Trays, 'Up to 10p' Lotto*

Philip & Tacey Ltd., *Cardboard Coins, Decimal Aid Coin and Symbol Insert Matching Cards, Decimal Aid Money Value Recognition Cards, Decimal Aid Value Matching Cards, Gummed Paper Money, Handy Coin Rubber Stamps, 'How much will it cost?' Rubber Stamps, 'Up to 20p' Dominoes*

# Chapter 12
# Capacity (C2)

National Curriculum
Attainment Target 2: Level 2
Attainment Target 2: Level 4
Attainment Target 8: Level 2
Attainment Target 8: Level 3
Attainment Target 13: Level 2

## For the teacher

The previous chapter on Capacity (Chapter 12 of *Nuffield Maths 1 Teachers' Handbook*) used non-standard units such as spoonfuls and cupfuls to measure the capacity or internal volume of a container. This chapter introduces the standard unit of capacity—the litre. The $\frac{1}{2}$ litre and $\frac{1}{4}$ litre are also introduced as convenient sub-units without calling them 500 and 250 millilitres respectively. The notion of volume is also extended to include the *space occupied* by a solid body as well as the *space inside* a hollow container. (The *capacity* of a thermos flask is the amount of liquid it will hold; the *volume* of the flask is the amount of space it occupies in a picnic basket.)

In all forms of measuring it is important that children have plenty of practice at estimating. Most children become adept at estimating length 'by eye' and weight 'by feel', but since a given quantity of liquid remains unchanged regardless of the shape of the container it is in, estimating capacity is much more difficult. Before proceeding with the introduction of the litre, the teacher may wish to know if a child has acquired the concept of conservation or invariance of quantity.

*Check-up on the invariance of quantity* This check-up will help the teacher to see how the child understands the idea that a given amount of water (or dry sand or rice, etc.) does not change when it is poured from one container to another.

You will need:
a jug of coloured liquid,
two glass beakers of the same size and shape,
one jar taller and narrower than the beakers,
one jar shorter and wider than the beakers.

Place the two beakers of same shape and size in front of the child. Pour some coloured liquid from a jug into one beaker until it is about half full.

Ask the child to pour the same amount from the jug into the other beaker. Ask, 'Have the two beakers got the same amount of liquid in them?' 'How do you know?'

Then ask him to pour the liquid from his beaker into the tall jar (or shallow jar). Put this by the side of your beaker containing liquid.

Ask whether your beaker and the tall jar have the same amount of liquid in them. If he says yes, ask him why he is sure. If he says no, he needs more experience with pouring and filling various containers with liquid.

## Summary of the stages

**C2**: 1    Introduction of the litre

**C2**: 2    Comparing a litre with non-standard measures

**C2**: 3    Introduction of $\frac{1}{2}$ litre and $\frac{1}{4}$ litre

**C2**: 4    Cubes, boxes and walls

## Vocabulary

Wide, wider, narrow, narrower, tall, taller, short, shorter, deep, deeper, shallow, shallower, full, empty, amount, more than, less than, as much as, about the same as, contains, container, beaker, jug, glass, capacity, volume, litre, half ($\frac{1}{2}$), quarter ($\frac{1}{4}$).

## Equipment and apparatus

Containers of all shapes and sizes, beakers, bottles, jars, buckets, cups, kettles, tea-pots, tubs, funnels, litre measures of various shapes. Fine dry sand, rice or lentils, etc. Plastic containers which can be cut down to a particular size are very useful.

## Working with the children

### C2: 1    Introduction of the litre

As with all measurement, the children should be led to see the *need* for a standard measure. A cupful at Uncle Joe's house might not be the same as a cupful at Grandma's and not all jugs or bottles hold the same amount. So we need to have a measure which is always the same. The children should be shown and allowed to use several litre containers of different shapes—a litre measuring-beaker, a litre bottle and a hollow cube which holds a litre. (See Appendix of this chapter for diagram showing how to make a litre cube suitable for dry materials such as sand, rice, etc.)

A selection of other containers such as cups, jugs, bottles, pans, kettles, buckets, bowls, etc., should be available so that the children can compare each with a litre container in order to discover if it holds more than a litre, less than a litre or about a litre. This should be done first by visual inspection and estimation and then by a practical method so that the containers are sorted into three subsets:

| These hold more than a litre. | These hold about a litre. | These hold less than a litre. |
|---|---|---|

In order to reduce the temptation to measure first and then go back and estimate (!), two separate worksheets are provided for recording. The first (C2: 1.1) is for the estimations and the second (C2: 1.2) for the practical measuring.

When carrying out these practical assignments, some children prefer to start with the litre measure full and then pour into the container being investigated.

This bowl holds less than 1 litre.

This bucket holds more than 1 litre.

Others may prefer to fill the container first and then pour into the litre measure, perhaps with the aid of a funnel. This method may prove difficult when larger vessels are involved.

It is extremely important that discussion follows these activities. Children's answers to such questions as 'Did you think that bowl held less than a litre before you tried it?' or 'If the bowl is full and there is some water left in the litre measure, does this mean the bowl holds less or more than a litre?' will give the teacher a useful insight into children's thinking about capacity.

This jug holds less than 1 litre.

This bottle holds more than 1 litre.

A display of several different shaped containers which all hold 1 litre—bottles, measuring cans, hollow boxes, plastic containers cut to size to that they just hold a litre—will help the children to appreciate that a litre does not always have to be of a certain shape.

If the children are already familiar with the kilogram they may be intrigued to discover that 1 litre of water weighs 1 kilogram. This can be shown either by balancing a litre jug of water against an empty litre jug and a kilogram weight, or by first standing an empty litre container on the kitchen scales, setting the dial to 'zero' and then pouring in 1 litre of water. Some may wish to experiment with a litre of sand or of rice to see if they are heavier or lighter than 1 kilogram.

*Worksheets should not be introduced until children have had plenty of practical experience and opportunity for discussion.*

**Capacity 2**
sheet 1.1

name
date

Find some containers like these:

a bowl    a mug    bottles    a bucket    a tin

Look at a litre measure.
Estimate if each container
holds: more than a litre,
or less than a litre,
or about a litre.

I estimate that:

The [bowl] holds [more than] a litre.

The [mug] holds [ ] a litre.

The [ ] holds [ ] a litre.

The [ ] holds [ ] a litre.

The [ ] holds [ ] a litre.

The [ ] holds [ ] a litre.

Nuffield Maths 2 Worksheets Pack K    Comparing with a litre by estimation

---

**Capacity 2** name ........... date ........... sheet 1.2

Use the same containers
you had for the last worksheet.

This time use a litre measure
to find out if each container
holds: more than a litre,
or less than a litre,
or about a litre.

I measured and found out:

The [bowl] holds [more than] a litre.

The [ ] holds [ ] a litre.

The [ ] holds [ ] a litre.

The [ ] holds [ ] a litre.

The [ ] holds [ ] a litre.

The [ ] holds [ ] a litre.

Nuffield Maths 2 Worksheets Pack K    Comparing with a litre by measuring

---

## C2: 2   Comparing a litre with non-standard measures

Having introduced the litre, it is a good idea to give the children experiences to help them to 'fix' its size in terms of containers with which they are familiar.

In the first instance, vessels holding less than a litre (a mug, cup, medicine bottle, yoghurt carton, beaker, paste pot, etc.) are used to arrive at such conclusions as 'It takes 5 of these mugfuls to fill a litre.' As before, the children should be encouraged to estimate first. If they find this difficult and are loath to 'have a go', sometimes it helps if they are allowed to pour one mugful into the litre measure 'to see where it comes up to.'

The practical result can be achieved either by starting with a full litre and counting how many times the small container can be filled from it or by continually filling the container and tipping it into the litre measure. In either case, some sort of tally should be kept. The worksheet C2: 2.2 suggests that a graph of the results is made. The questions relating to the graph may promote some interesting discussion because, in this instance, the container which has to be used *most* and has the *highest* column on the graph is the one which holds *least*. This leads to the idea that 'the more times you have to use the container to fill a litre, the less the container holds' or 'if the capacity of the container is bigger, you need a smaller number of pourings.'

This might be a good opportunity for emphasising yet again how unsatisfactory a 'cupful' is as a measure and how important it is to have a standard measure.

Next, the children should be given experience of the use of the litre to measure larger capacities. Such containers as a bowl, a bucket, a watering can, a baby's bath, large plastic containers, perhaps an oil can or even a fish tank should be investigated to first estimate and then measure to find how many litres each will hold.

Pouring from large containers might prove difficult. It is easier to keep count of the number of times a full litre jug can be emptied into each container. Again some sort of tally should be kept and a graph drawn to display how many litres each container holds. As before, the estimating is

**Example**

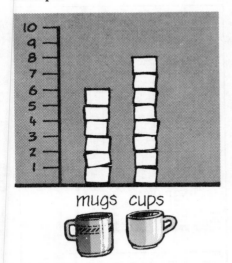

mugs  cups

It takes 6 mugs to fill a litre.
It takes 8 cups to fill a litre.

The cup holds *less* than the mug.

quite difficult so perhaps pouring in just one litre might be allowed before an estimate is made. The estimating and measuring activities are dealt with in separate worksheets (C2: 2.3 and C2: 2.4), so the children will require the same collection of containers for both sheets. Inevitably the situation will arise when the container being measured is full and the last litre jug has been only partly emptied into it. This will illustrate the need for smaller sub-units such as the $\frac{1}{2}$ litre and $\frac{1}{4}$ litre which are dealt with in the next section.

*Worksheets should not be introduced until children have had plenty of practical experience and opportunity for discussion.*

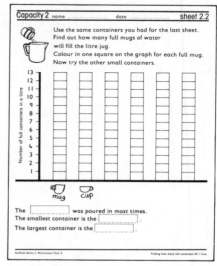

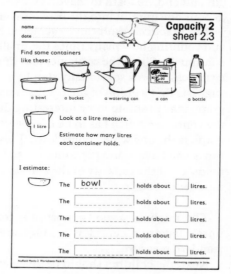

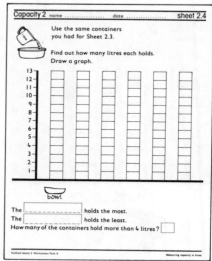

## C2: 3  Introduction of the ½ litre and ¼ litre

Taking the half-litre first, the children should be given ample opportunity to convince themselves that a litre just fills two ½-litre containers and, conversely, that two ½-litres are just enough to fill a 1-litre measure. The word 'half' and the symbol ½ should both be introduced stressing that ½ means:

$$\frac{1}{2}$$  ← 1 whole litre divided into ← 2 *equal* parts

Other examples of 'halves' could usefully be mentioned at this point, (half a kilogram, half an hour, half of 10 is 5 etc.), especially if it helps to emphasise that 2 halves make 1 whole and that the two halves are *equal*. (Children often talk about having 'the biggest half'!)

Activities similar to those used to introduce the litre can be repeated for the ½ litre. (See Appendix to this chapter for diagram showing how to make a ½-litre container suitable for dry materials.) This time the children should be able to sort containers into sub-sets: 'holds more than ½ litre', 'holds less than ½ litre' and 'holds about ½ litre'. Some children may be able to find a set of containers which 'hold at least ½ litre but less than 1 litre'.

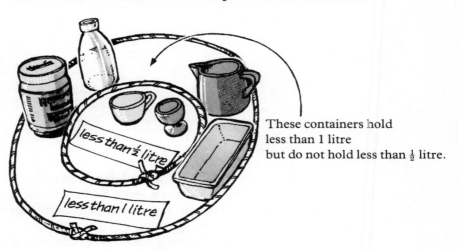

These containers hold less than 1 litre but do not hold less than ½ litre.

When attempting the worksheet involving comparison with the ½-litre (C2: 3.1), the children should use the same small containers they used for the 1 litre comparison. After estimating and then measuring, the results should be compared with those obtained on worksheet C2: 2.2. Even allowing for the fact that no measuring is exact, some relationship between the number of cups required to fill the 1 litre jug and the ½ litre jug should be apparent, for example 8 cups to fill the 1 litre jug, 4 cups to fill the ½ litre jug.

This link with number is developed in worksheet C2: 3.2.

When introducing the quarter-litre both the word 'quarter' and the symbol '¼' should be used, again the children should be given the opportunity of experimenting with 1 litre, ½ litre and ¼ litre containers in order to discover for themselves the relationships which exist:

2 ½ litres make a 1 litre
4 ¼ litres make a 1 litre
2 ¼ litres make a ½ litre

These relationships can be developed further by appealing to number patterns:

| Number of litres | 1 | 2 | 3 | 4 | 5 | |
|---|---|---|---|---|---|---|
| Number of $\frac{1}{2}$ litres | 2 | 4 | 6 | 8 | 10 | |
| Number of $\frac{1}{4}$ litres | 4 | 8 | 12 | 16 | 20 | etc. |

*Worksheets should not be introduced until children have had plenty of practical experience and opportunity for discussion.*

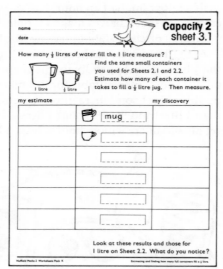

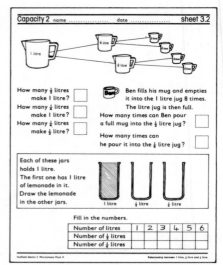

### C2 : 4  Cubes, boxes and walls

So far the emphasis has been on the space inside a container—the internal volume. This section extends the idea of volume to include space occupied by solid bodies.

The early activities of children using bricks, blocks, plasticine, etc. to build castles or make models all play an essential part in grasping the idea of invariance of volume—that is the acceptance that the space filled remains unchanged despite rearrangement of the parts or of the shape. At the child's level, it is useful to know if he realised that two solid shapes may each 'take up the same space' even though they look different.

*Check-up on the invariance of volume*  The child is given 24 cubes all the same size and asked to make two piles with the same number of cubes in each. How does he know? Ask the child to use the cubes in one pile to build a wall or a block and then to use the other pile to build another wall or block which looks the same as the first. Do they both take up the same amount of space? Move one set of cubes to make a new shape.

Do the two sets *still* take up the same amount of space?

If he says yes, ask him why he is sure.

Answers such as, 'The blocks were the same at the start. They still have the same amount of wood in each,' show that the child has grasped the concept.

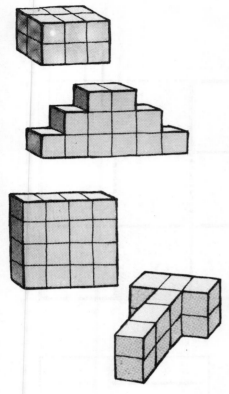

If he says no, then he requires more experience of building different shapes with the same number of bricks.

No worksheets are provided for this section. Pictures or diagrams attempting to portray 3-dimensional shapes on flat paper may confuse children because some of the cubes may not be visible in the pictures. In the case of the first picture, for instance, most adults would accept that it represents 12 cubes arranged in a block but a child might say that there are only 10 because that is all he can see.

At this stage, it is the actual manipulation of the cubes which is most valuable. Recording of a sort may be in the form of a display of blocks or 'walls' each containing the same number of cubes.

To give children some experience which will lead them towards 'invariance of volume', it may be helpful to provide a number of open boxes of different shapes, but which all hold the same number of cubes, 24 for example. These boxes will probably have to be made or cut from existing boxes. Although the boxes look different the child will find he can just pack the same number of cubes in each.

Similar experience may be gained from two pieces of plasticine which are balanced on a pair of scales and then moulded into shapes which look the same. One piece is then formed into a different shape which still takes up the same amount of space.

*No worksheets are published for this stage.*

## References and resources

Nuffield Mathematics Teaching Project, Beginnings ▽, Shape and Size ▽, Nuffield Guides, Chambers/Murray 1967 (See Introduction page vii)

Williams, M. E., *Come and Measure—Capacity*, Macmillan 1975

E. J. Arnold, *Measuring Volume Kit, Plastic Funnels, Plastic Measuring Beakers, Plastic Measuring Cones, Plastic Measuring Cylinders*

Osmiroid, *Graduated Capacity Measures* ($\frac{1}{4}$, $\frac{1}{2}$ and $2 \times 1$ litre)

Philip & Tacey Ltd, *Metric Aid Measuring Jug, Metric Aluminium Liquid Measures*

Taskmaster, *Graduated Cylinders, Graduated Jugs, Graduated Measures, Metric Capacity Containers, Metric Pails*

# Appendix

*Construction of 1 litre and ½ litre containers from stiff paper, without glue.*

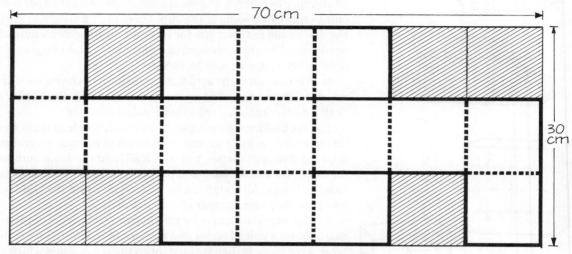

Net for 1 litre open box.    Squares 10 cm × 10 cm

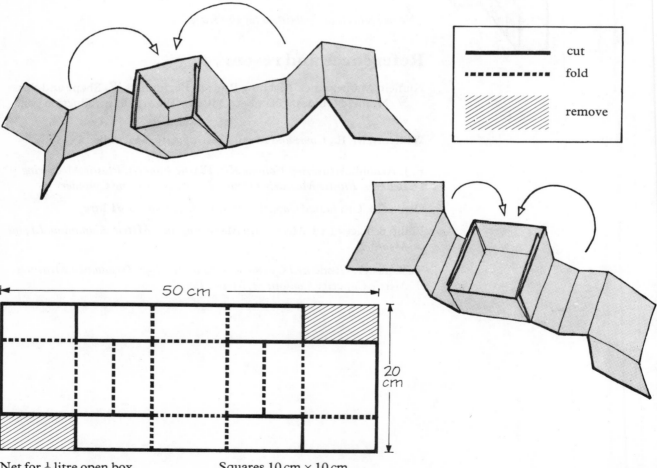

| | cut |
| --- | --- |
| | fold |
| | remove |

Net for ½ litre open box.

Squares 10 cm × 10 cm
Oblongs 10 cm × 5 cm

# Chapter 13
# The language of probability (P2)

National Curriculum
Attainment Target 14: Level 2
Attainment Target 14: Level 3

## For the teacher

The activities of this chapter invite children to say what they think will be the outcome of a single random event. They should be encouraged to use and understand some of the language of probability such as

*It is impossible that . . .; It is likely that . . .; It is certain that . . .*

These expressions are three of the links in the chain which will eventually form a probability scale. Gradually, more, smaller links will be introduced and, much later, these links may be given numerical values ranging from 0 (impossible) to 1 (certain).

## Summary of the stages

1  Impossible, likely, certain.

2  How likely?

## Vocabulary

Possible, probable, perhaps, impossible, very unlikely, likely, very likely, certain, just as likely, equally likely, more likely, less likely.

It is important to remember that, in the context of probability, the opposite of **impossible** is not possible but **certain** and the opposite of **certain** is not uncertain but **impossible**.

## Equipment and apparatus

Different coloured counters, balls, interlocking cubes, card for making small picture cards, playing cards, string and pegs for a washing line, plastic bags or transparent envelopes, cloth bag.

## Working with the children

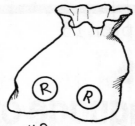

### 1 Impossible, likely, certain

Put two red balls in a bag and invite
a child to draw out one ball without
looking and ask,

Are you certain to pick out a red ball?

Is it possible to pick out a blue ball?

Now place a red ball and a blue ball
in the bag and draw one out without
looking.

Is it likely that you will
pick a red ball?

Is it likely that you will
pick a blue ball?

Is it possible to pick out a yellow ball?

Are you certain to pick out a ball
that is not green?

This time place three red balls and
one blue ball in the bag and draw
one out without looking.

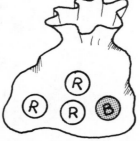

Which colour are you
more likely to pick?

Which colour are you less likely to pick?

Which colour is it impossible to pick?

This sort of activity can be repeated by drawing one card from a set—not
necessarily a full pack—of playing cards held face down. First let the
children see how many of each colour, red or black, are in the set. Start
with the same number of red and black cards and then increase one colour
while reducing the other so that the children will be led to see that when
there are more reds in the set you are *more likely* to draw a red card. If all
the cards are red you will be *certain* to draw a red card and it will be
*impossible* to pick a black one.

The *Escape* game could be played first with a group of children in the hall with a PE mat as the 'river', a PE bench as the garden wall and numbered footprints or paper 'slabs' as the path. Once the children are familiar with the game, they can play in pairs on the worksheet using a white counter or cube to represent the walker.

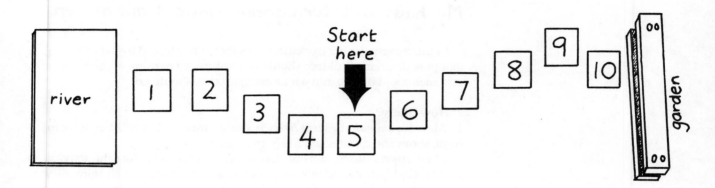

As before, make sure the children have a chance to match and compare the red counters with the blue and green counters before they are placed in the bag. Examples of children's talk might be:

'There are more reds, so you are (more) likely to pick a red.'

'She (probably) will not pick a blue because there aren't (so) many of them.'

'She might (is likely to) pick a blue or a green because . . .'

Through playing the game and talking about it the children should come to realise that although red is the *more likely* colour to be drawn from the bag than either of the other two colours, a 'not red' counter (a blue or a green) is *equally likely* or *just as likely* to be drawn as a red counter.

In the sorting activity, small cards on which statements are written and perhaps pictures drawn are placed in the correct hoop.

Some possible sentences are:

It will get dark tonight.

I will see a dog on the way home.

My hair will turn green while I am asleep.

In the corresponding worksheet, this idea is reinforced by using a mapping diagram. Children should be encouraged to think of their own statements and decide into which category they should go.

### 2 How likely?

In *Make an animal*, the term *likely* is sub-divided so that children have to think about and discuss *how likely* an event is.

The cards should be laid out, face up, for discussion before the activity begins. Children should talk about how many there are of each animal—9 pigs, 5 sheep, 3 hens and 1 horse—in order to appreciate which animal card is *more likely* to be turned up from the top of the pile. In the first instance, return each card to the pack and re-shuffle before the next choice is made.

Keeping a tally score of the number of times each animal is chosen

pigs ⳠⳠⳠ I     sheep III     hens I     horses O

will help the children sort the cards into the different categories.

| Very unlikely | Unlikely | Likely | Very likely |
|---|---|---|---|
| | | | |

As an alternative to making cards, a 'feely bag' and coloured counters or cubes could be used to represent the animals with perhaps pink for pigs, white for sheep, brown for hens and black for the horse.

Later on, the activity can be made more interesting by **not** returning the chosen cards but by leaving them exposed. The likelihood of a certain animal card being selected now changes as the game proceeds. For example, if the horse card has already been chosen, it is now *impossible* for it to be selected from the remaining cards in the pack. If it can be seen that 4 pigs but no sheep have been chosen, there are 5 pigs and 5 sheep left in the pack so now it is *just as likely* or *equally likely* that a pig or a sheep will be chosen.

In order to widen the scope of '*likely*' still further, the *Washing line* activity could be used with a group of children before they go on to the worksheet for reinforcement. Sentence cards are placed in one of the pockets on the washing line.

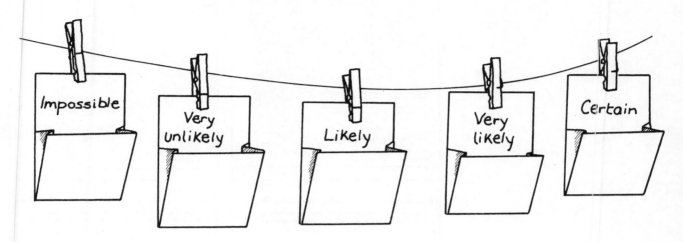

Some sentences might be:

| I shall watch television to-night. |
| --- |

| I shall get £20 pocket money this week. |
| --- |

| I shall be eight before I am seven. |
| --- |

| It will snow next Christmas day. |
| --- |

| Friday will come after Thursday. |
| --- |

Again, children should be encouraged to suggest their own sentences.

157

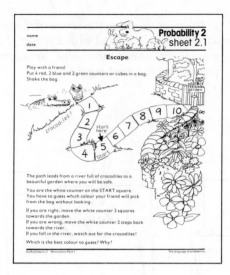

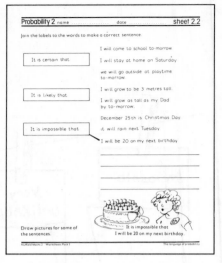

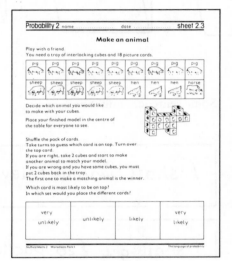

*Worksheets should not be introduced until children have had plenty of practical experience and opportunity for discussion.*

## References and resources

Nuffield Maths Teaching Project, *Probability and Statistics*, Nuffield Guide Chambers/Murray 1969 (see Introduction page vii)

# Index

angle 99
area 92
area, conservation of 94, 95
array 56, 70, 71

balance scales 107
base ten 12
boundary 92

calendar 127
candle clock 118
certain 154
change, giving 140
circumference 78
clock face, a home-made 130–1
clocks, non-mechanical 117
coin recognition 133–4
columns 16, 17
commutative law 56, 59
counting back 1, 4, 45
counting on 4, 30, 33–5, 73, 140

'dead-length' rulers 78
decimetre 77
dial reading 118
difference, finding the
   2, 3, 44, 140
division (inverse of multiplication)
   70–1
division (repeated subtraction)
   65, 67–8
division (sharing) 66, 67

equals '=' sign, the 29, 40
equals '=' sign, misuses of 41
equation 36, 37
equivalence relation 29
equivalent sets 51, 52
equivalent value (of coins) 134–6
estimating numbers up to 20 38

faces 88–90

grouping activities 13–6
grouping games 69
grouping in fours 15
grouping in tens 21

grouping in threes 14

hexagon 84

impossible 154
inset boards 133
invariance of quantity 144
invariance of volume 150

kitchen scales 110

likely 154

mapping 1, 47
mass 106
metre sticks 75
money dominoes 133
multiplication (as repeated
   addition) 53
multiplication square 61

number bonds 30, 31, 48
number line
   4, 8, 20–3, 33, 37, 45, 48, 54, 69
number sentences 7, 36
number sequences 4
number strip 33
number system 21
numerical card-holder 24

octagon 84
one to one correspondence 12

pentagon 84
perimeter 78, 95
picture problems 7
pin-timer 118
place value 12, 29
plane shapes 84, 85
prism 85
probability 153

recipes 112–3
reflection 102
reflexive property 42
reflexive relation 42
remainders 72

right angle 100
rotation 99

sand timer 117
shadow stick 117
shopping bills 138
sorting (for shape and size)
   83–5
standard measure 75
standard units 106
story problems 7
subtraction oblongs 48
subtraction squares 48
symbol '−' 1, 8
symbol '+' 70
symbol '×' 57
symmetrical patterns 97
symmetric property 42
symmetric relations 41
symmetry, axis of 96, 97
symmetry, first ideas of 96–7

'table facts' up to 30 59
'take away' problems 5, 6, 46
three-dimensional figures 104–5
three dimensional objects 88, 92
three dimensional shapes 86
time, telling the 121–5
time, ways of measuring 117
transitive property 42
transitive relations 42
translation 102
trundle wheel 76
two-digit numerals 12, 29
two-dimensional shapes 86

unlikely 156

vertical subtraction 1, 9, 47
volume, internal 144, 149

water clock 117

zero cards 16, 20

# Nuffield Maths 5–11

## Nuffield Maths 1 Teachers' Handbook

12:1
13:1
13:2

**Key 12:1** denotes National Curriculum
Attainment Target 12: Level 1

## Contents

**1 Sets and relations (N1)**
12:1  N1:1  Relations (different types of correspondence)
13:1  N1:2  Early sorting experiences—leading to sets
13:2  N1:3  Sorting into subsets
      N1:4  Sorting—two criteria

**2 Matching (N2)**
2:1   N2:1  Matching to find equivalent sets
13:1  N2:2a Two non-equivalent sets
      N2:2b Three non-equivalent sets
      N2:3  Pictorial representation and semi-tallying

**3 Counting and numerals (N3)**
2:1   N3:1  Counting
      N3:2  Matching a number symbol to a set
      N3:3  Introducing number words
      N3:4  The empty set
      N3:5  Conservation of number

**4 Ordering (N4)**
5:1   N4:1  Ordinal numbers
12:2  N4:2  Putting non-equivalent sets in order
13:2  N4:3  Signs 'is greater than', 'is less than'
      N4:4  Tallying and pictorial representation

**5 Towards addition (N5)**
3:1   N5:1  Composition of small numbers
5:2           1a bead bag  1b duck pond  1c rods or strips and frames
      N5:2a Addition of two disjoint sets; putting sets together
      N5:2b Addition of two disjoint sets, using structured apparatus
      N5:3  Recording addition by mapping

**6 Addition to 10 (N6)**
3:1   N6:1  Number bonds up to 10
3:2   N6:2  Counting on
4:1   N6:3  Patterns in simple addition
5:1   N6:4  Picture problems—additions
5:2   N6:5  Introduction of addition sign and vertical addition
6:2   N6:6  The addition square
      N6:7  Estimation of numbers up to 10

**7 Length (L1)**
8:1   L1:1  Descriptive language
8:2   L1:2  Comparing two unequal lengths
      L1:3a Matching lengths: matching two objects of about the same length
      L1:3b Matching lengths: using several objects to 'make up' a length
      L1:4  Ordering
      L1:5  Measuring with repeated units
      L1:6  Using limb measures

**8 Shape and space (S1)**
10:1  S1:1  Awareness of shape and space, extension of vocabulary
10:2  S1:2  Early sorting of 3-D shapes
11:1  S1:3  Early sorting of 2-D shapes
12:1  **Appendix**

**9 Weighing (W1)**
8:1   W1:1  Descriptive language—heavy and light
8:2   W1:2  Comparing—heavier than and lighter than
13:2  W1:3  Balancing
      W1:4  Ordering

**10 Time (T1)**
8:1   T1:1  Association—matching events to daytime or night-time
8:2   T1:2  Putting time sequence in order
13:2  T1:3a Comparisons: fast and slow
      T1:3b Comparisons: timing
      T1:4  Graphs and charts

**11 Money (M1)**
3:1   M1:1  Recognition of 1p, 2p, 5p, 10p coins
5:2   M1:2  Comparison of amounts of money (a) by matching (b) by totals
8:2   M1:3  Using coins to make amounts up to 10p
      M1:4  Early stages of shopping
      **Appendix**: Suggestions for shops in schools

**12 Capacity (C1)**
8:1   C1:1  Full, empty and half empty
8:2   C1:2  Which holds more? (visual judgement)
12:1  C1:3  Finding the capacity by counting
13:2  C1:4  Sorting containers
      C1:5a Comparing by emptying
      C1:5b Comparing by filling

**13 Beginning probability**
5:2   P1:1  Yes, no, perhaps
14:1  P1:2  Can you tell?
      P1:3  Odds and evens

## Nuffield Maths 2 Teachers' Handbook

3:2
5:2

**Key 3:2** denotes National Curriculum
Attainment Target 3: Level 2

## Contents

**1 Early stages of subtraction (N7)**
3:2   N7:1  Finding the difference
5:2   N7:2  Counting back
      N7:3  Taking away
      N7:4  Recording subtraction
      N7:5  Practice sheets

**2 A first look at place value (N8)**
2:2   N8:1  Early grouping activities and games
2:4   N8:2  Grouping using cubes, etc.
4:3   N8:3  Grouping in tens

**3 Addition to 20 (N9)**
3:2   N9:1  Number bonds up to 20
3:3   N9:2  Counting on
4:2   N9:3  Ways of recording
5:1   N9:4  Estimation of numbers up to 20

**4 Subtraction involving numbers up to 20 (N10)**
3:2   N10:1 Difference by matching and counting
3:3   N10:2 Subtraction by counting back
5:3   N10:3 Taking away
6:2   N10:4 Ways of recording

**5 Introducing multiplication (N11)**
3:3   N11:1 Recognising and counting equivalent sets
5:3   N11:2 Multiplication as repeated addition
12:2  N11:3 Arrays and the commutative law
      N11:4 Activities and games for 'table facts' up to 30

**6 Introducing division (N12)**
3:3   N12:1 The sharing aspect of division
4:3   N12:2 The repeated subtraction aspect of division
      N12:3 Division as the inverse of multiplication
      N12:4 Remainders

**7 Length (L2)**
2:2   L2:1  Appreciating the need for a standard measure
2:4   L2:2  Introduction of the metre
8:2   L2:3  Comparison with a 10 cm rod (decimetre)
8:3   L2:4  Measuring in centimetres—straight and curved lines
13:2  L2:5  Personal measurements in m and cm
13:3

**8 Shape and Space (S2)**
10:1  S2:1  Sorting for shape and size
10:2  S2:2  Fitting shapes together
10:3  S2:3  Surfaces and faces
11:2  S2:4  Covering surfaces—leading to area
12:1  S2:5  First ideas of symmetry
      S2:6  Angles and rotation

**9 Weighing (W2)**
2:2   W2:1  Introduction of kilogram and ½ kilogram
2:4   W2:2  Using the kilogram and ½ kilogram
8:2   W2:3  Introduction of the 100 gram weight
8:3
13:2
13:3

**10 Time (T2)**
2:2   T2:1  Ways of measuring time
2:4   T2:2  Reading a dial
8:2   T2:3  Telling the time (hours, halves, quarters)
13:2  T2:4  Telling the time (five-minute intervals)
13:3  T2:5  Simple calculations involving time
      T2:6  Other units of time

**11 Money (M2)**
3:2   M2:1  Reinforcement of coins up to 10p and introduction of 50p
5:2   M2:2  Breakdown of coins—equivalent values
8:2   M2:3  Making amounts up to 20p
13:2  M2:4  Addition—simple shopping bills
      M2:5  Giving change and finding difference by counting on
      M2:6  Subtraction by taking away

**12 Capacity (C2)**
2:2   C2:1  Introduction of the litre
2:4   C2:2  Comparing a litre with non-standard measure
8:2   C2:3  Introduction of ½ litre and ¼ litre
8:3   C2:4  Cubes, boxes and walls
13:2

**13 The language of probability**
14:2  P2:1  Impossible, likely, certain
14:3  P2:2  How likely?

## *Nuffield Maths 3  Teachers' Handbook*

| 2:2 |
| 3:1 |

**Key 2:2** denotes National Curriculum
Attainment Target **2**: Level **2**

# Contents

| 2:2 |
| 3:1 |

**1 Addition 1**
 1 Pairs that make 10
 2 Making an addition square
 3 A useful discovery (the commutative property)

| 10:2 |
| 10:4 |
| 11:3 |
| 12:1 |

**2 Shape 1**
 1 Sorting and classifying—straight and curved lines
 2 Plane shapes with 3 or more sides
 3 Axes of symmetry

| 2:4 |
| 4:3 |

**3 Place Value**
 1 Tallying
 2 Place value—practical examples

| 8:3 |
| 10:2 |
| 12:1 |
| 13:2 |
| 13:3 |

**4 Length 1**
 1 Measuring with parts of the body (estimating before measuring)
 2 Measuring with more than one unit
 3 Towards a standard measure
 4 The metre
 5 The 10-centimetre (decimetre) rod

| 2:4 |
| 3:4 |
| 5:3 |
| 6:2 |
| 6:3 |
| 12:3 |

**5 Addition 2**
 1 Counting on from 10, 20, 30 . . .
 2 The associative property of addition
 3 Patterns in addition
 4 Inequalities
 5 Practice activities
  a) magic squares
  b) the 'computer'

| 8:2 |

**6 Money 1**
 1 A close look at our coins
 2 Analysis of coin values (making up the value of a coin)
 3 Using coins to make up amounts
 4 Finding the missing coin
 5 Giving change by counting on

| 3:4 |
| 6:2 |

**7 Subtraction 1**
 1 Difference
 2 Taking away
 3 Counting back

| 8:3 |
| 13:2 |
| 13:3 |

**8 Weight 1**
 1 Experience of 'heaviness' leading to the simple balance
 2 Using a school balance—estimating activities
 3 Comparing the weight of materials
 4 Towards the concept of conservation
 5 Towards a standardised measure
 6 The kilogram and half-kilogram

| 3:3 |
| 3:4 |
| 5:3 |
| 5:4 |
| 6:2 |

**9 Multiplication 1**
 1 Reinforcing multiplication—as repeated addition
 2 Introducing factors and products
 3 Hops of the same size along a number line/track
 4 Patterns in multiplication
 5 Rows and columns as an introduction to commutativity

| 8:2 |
| 8:3 |

**10 Time 1**
 1 The minute divisions of the clock face
 2 Simple fractions of an hour
 3 Counting any whole number of minutes

| 13:2 |

**11 Capacity 1**
 1 Comparison of capacity of vessels. (Which holds the most?)
 2 Measuring capacity using suitable arbitrary measures
 3 Development of conservation—using a fixed amount of liquid in varying shaped containers

| 3:3 |
| 3:4 |

**12 Division 1**
 1 Division by sharing
 2 Division by repeated subtraction

| 7:4 |
| 11:4 |

**13 Addresses on a grid**
 1 Addresses by counting across and up
 2 Naming squares on a map
 3 Codes

| 10:3 |
| 10:4 |
| 11:3 |

**14 Shape 2**
 1 Experiences with three-dimensional objects—curved and flat surfaces—edges, faces and corners
 2 Counting faces, edges and corners
 3 Fitting solids together

| 2:4 |
| 3:4 |
| 5:2 |
| 6:3 |
| 12:3 |

**15 Subtraction 2**
 1 Patterns in subtraction
 2 Complementary addition ('making up the difference')
 3 Word problems

| 2:3 |
| 3:3 |

**16 Money 2**
 1 Counting up amounts—5p coins. counting amounts of mixed coins.
 2 Going shopping—some vocabulary used when buying and selling Bills and simple multiplication and division examples
 3 Payment and change
  a) Giving change by counting on
  b) Selecting coins and receiving change
  c) Checking your change

| 3:3 |
| 3:4 |
| 5:3 |
| 5:4 |

**17 Multiplication 2**
 1 More rows and columns—commutativity
 2 Square numbers
 3 Learning multiplication tables—making a start
 4 Vertical layout of multiplication
 5 Magic squares

| 2:4 |
| 8:3 |
| 8:4 |

**18 Length 2**
 1 Measuring lines in centimetres
 2 Drawing lines the correct length
 3 Measuring distances and curved lines
 4 Measuring lengths up to 100 cm
  a) using a metre rule
  b) using a shorter rule
 5 Addition and subtraction of centimetres

| 2:2 |
| 5:4 |

**19 Introducing fractions 1**
 1 Dividing shapes into equal parts
 2 Fractions of measures
 3 Fractions from sets

| 8:2 |

**20 Time 2**
 1 Counting hours. Telling the time in whole numbers of hours ('o'clock')
 2 Between the hours—all number notation—relation of digital displays to clock hand position—continuous movement of the hour hand
 3 Time past and to the hour
 4 Calculation of intervals of time, including some greater than 1 hour
 5 Strange faces—a diversion introducing non-standard clock faces

| 3:3 |
| 3:4 |
| 4:3 |
| 5:3 |

**21 Division 2**
 1 Division and multiplication
 2 Division with remainders

| 8:3 |
| 13:2 |
| 13:3 |

**22 Weight 2**
 1 The hecto (100 g) weight
 2 The hecto as part of the kilogram
 3 Using hecto weights
 4 Using kilogram weights—weighing people
 5 Using smaller weights—less than 100 g

| 8:4 |

**23 Area**
 1 Comparing surfaces
 2 Which shapes cover best?
 3 Area by Counting squares

| 8:3 |
| 8:4 |

**24 Capacity 2 and Volume**
 1 Standard measures of capacity—the litre and half litre (500 ml)
 2 Cuboids, cubes and volume

| 14:3 |

**25 Probability**
 1 Getting to know dice
 2 Fair and unfair
 3 Biased dice

## Pupils' Record Sheet 1

| AT:Level | Statement of attainment | Chapters in Teachers' Handbook One | | | | | | | | | | | | |
|---|---|---|---|---|---|---|---|---|---|---|---|---|---|---|
| | | 1 | 2 | 3 | 4 | 5 | 6 | 7 | 8 | 9 | 10 | 11 | 12 | 13 |
| 2:1a | ● Count, read, write and order numbers up to at least 10; know that the size of a set is given by the last number in the count. | | | ○ | | | | | | | | | | |
| 2:1b | ● Understand the conservation of number. | | ○ | ○ | | | | | | | | | | |
| 3:1 | ● Add and subtract, using objects where the numbers involved are no greater than 10. | | | | | ○ | ○ | | | | | ○ | | |
| 3:2a | ● Know and use addition and subtraction facts up to 10. | | | | | | ○ | | | | | | | |
| 4:1 | ● Give a sensible estimate of a small number of objects (up to 10). | | | | | | ○ | | | | | | | |
| 5:1 | ● Copy, continue and devise repeating patterns represented by objects/apparatus or one-digit numbers. | | | | | ○ | ○ | | | | | | | |
| 5:2a | ● Explore and use the patterns in addition and subtraction facts to 10. | | | | | ○ | ○ | | | | | ○ | | |
| 5:2b | ● Distinguish between odd and even numbers. | | | | | | | | | | | | | ○ |
| 6:2 | ● Understand the use of a symbol for an unknown number. | | | | | | ○ | | | | | | | |
| 8:1 | ● Compare and order objects without measuring, and use appropriate language. | | | | | | | ○ | | ○ | ○ | ○ | | |
| 8:2a | ● Use non-standard measures in length, area, volume, capacity, weight and time to compare objects and recognise the need to use standard units. | | | | | | | ○ | | ○ | ○ | ○ | | |
| 8:2b | ● Know how to use coins in simple contexts. | | | | | | | | | | | ○ | | |
| 10:1a | ● Sort 3-D and 2-D shapes. | | | | | | | | ○ | | | | | |
| 10:1b | ● Build with 3-D solid shapes and draw 2-D shapes and describe them. | | | | | | | | ○ | | | | | |
| 10:2a | ● Recognise squares, rectangles, circles, triangles, hexagons, pentagons, cubes, rectangular boxes (cuboids), cylinders, spheres, and describe them. | | | | | | | | ○ | | | | | |
| 11:1a | ● State a position using prepositions such as: on, inside, above, under, behind, next to, etc. | | | | | | | | ○ | | | | | |
| 11:1b | ● Give and understand instructions for moving along a line. | | | | | | | | ○ | | | | | |
| 12:1 | ● Select criteria for sorting a set of objects and apply consistently. | ○ | | | | | | | ○ | | | | ○ | |
| 12:2a | ● Choose criteria to sort and classify objects: record results of observations or outcomes of events. | | | | ○ | | | | | | | | | |
| 13:1a | ● Record with real objects or drawings and comment about the result. | ○ | ○ | | | | | | | | | | | |
| 13:1b | ● Create simple mapping diagrams showing relationships; read and interpret them. | ○ | ○ | | | | | | | | | | | |
| 13:2a | ● Construct, read and interpret block graphs and frequency tables. | | | | | ○ | | | | | ○ | ○ | ○ | |
| 13:2b | ● Use diagrams to represent the result of classifying using two different criteria. | ○ | | | | | | | | | | | | |
| 14:1 | ● Recognise possible outcomes of simple random events. | | | | | | | | | | | | | ○ |

The use of materials in practical tasks and real life problems (Attainment Targets 1 and 9) is built into the philosophy of the scheme throughout the *Nuffield Maths Teachers' Handbooks*, *Bronto Books* and *Challengers* series.

## Pupils' Record Sheet 2

| AT:Level | Statement of attainment | Chapters in Teachers' Handbook Two | | | | | | | | | | | | |
|---|---|---|---|---|---|---|---|---|---|---|---|---|---|---|
| | | 1 | 2 | 3 | 4 | 5 | 6 | 7 | 8 | 9 | 10 | 11 | 12 | 13 |
| 2:2a | read, write and order numbers to at least 100; use the knowledge that the tens-digit indicates the number of tens. | | ◡ | | | | | | | | | | | |
| 2:2b | understand the meaning of 'a half' and 'a quarter'. | | | | | | | ○ | | ○ | ○ | | ○ | |
| 2:4d | recognise and understand everyday fractions. | | | | | | | ◡ | | ◡ | ◡ | | ◡ | |
| 2:4f | understand and use the relationship between place values in whole numbers. | | ○ | | | | | | | | | | | |
| 3:2a | know and use addition and subtraction facts up to 10. | ◡ | | | | | | | | | | | | |
| 3:2b | compare two numbers and find the difference. | ○ | | | | | | | | | | | | |
| 3:2c | solve whole number problems involving addition and subtraction, including money. | | | ○ | ○ | | | | | | | ○ | | |
| 3:3a | know and use addition and subtraction facts up to 20 (including zero). | | | ○ | ○ | | | | | | | | | |
| 3:3b | solve problems involving multiplication or division of whole numbers of money; using a calculator where necessary. | | | | | ○ | ○ | | | | | | | |
| 3:3c | know and use multiplication facts up to 5 × 5, and all those in 2, 5 and 10 multiplication tables. | | | | | ○ | | | | | | | | |
| 4:2 | make a sensible estimate of a number of objects up to 20. | . | | ○ | | | | | | | | | | |
| 4:3a | recognise that the first digit is the most important in indicating the size of a number, and approximate to the nearest 10 or 100. | | ◡ | | | | | | | | | | | |
| 4:3b | understand 'remainders' given the context of calculation, and know whether to round up or down. | | | | | | ◡ | | | | | | | |
| 5:1 | copy, continue and devise repeating patterns represented by objects/apparatus or one-digit numbers. | | | ○ | | | | | | | | | | |
| 5:2a | explore and use the patterns in addition and subtraction facts to 10. | ○ | | | | | | | | | | ○ | | |
| 5:3a | explain number patterns and predict subsequent numbers where appropriate. | | | | | ○ | ○ | | | | | | | |
| 6:2 | understand the use of a symbol to stand for an unknown number. | | | | ○ | | | | | | | | | |
| 8:2a | use non-standard measures in length, area, volume, capacity, weight and time to compare objects and recognise the need to use standard units. | | | | | | | ○ | | ○ | ○ | | ○ | |
| 8:2b | know how to use coins in simple contexts. | | | | | | | | | | | ○ | | |
| 8:2c | know the most commonly used units in length, capacity, weight and time, and what they are used for. | | | | | | | ○ | | ○ | ○ | | ○ | |
| 8:3a | use a wider range of metric units. | | | | | | | ○ | | ○ | | | ○ | |

*Pupils' Record Sheet 2 continued*

| AT:Level | Statement of attainment | Chapters in Teachers' Handbook Two | | | | | | | | | | | | |
|---|---|---|---|---|---|---|---|---|---|---|---|---|---|---|
| | | 1 | 2 | 3 | 4 | 5 | 6 | 7 | 8 | 9 | 10 | 11 | 12 | 13 |
| 10:1b | • build with 3-D solid shapes and draw 2-D shapes and describe them. | | | | | | | | ○ | | | | | |
| 10:2a | • recognise squares, rectangles, circles, triangles, hexagons, pentagons, cubes, rectangular boxes (cuboids), cylinders, spheres, and describe them. | | | | | | | | ○ | | | | | |
| 10:2b | • recognise right-angled corners in 2-D and 3-D shapes. | | | | | | | | ○ | | | | | |
| 10:3 | • sort 2-D and 3-D shapes in different ways and give reasons for each method of sorting. | | | | | | | | ◡ | | | | | |
| 11:2a | • understand the notion of an angle. | | | | | | | | ○ | | | | | |
| 11:2b | • give and understand instructions for turning through right-angles. | | | | | | | | ○ | | | | | |
| 11:2c | • recognise different types of movement; straight movement (translation); turning (rotation); flip movement (reflection). | | | | | | | | ○ | | | | | |
| 12:1 | • select criteria for sorting a set of objects and apply consistently. | | | | | | | | ○ | | | | | |
| 12:2a | • choose criteria to sort and classify objects; record results of observations or outcomes of events. | | | | | ○ | | | | | | | | |
| 12:2b | • help to design a data collection sheet and use it to record a set of data leading to a frequency table. | | | | | ○ | | | | | | | | |
| 13:2 | • construct, read and interpret block graphs and frequency tables. | | | | | | | ○ | | ○ | ○ | ○ | | |
| 13:3 | • construct and interpret bar charts. | | | | | | | ◡ | | ◡ | ◡ | | | |
| 14:2 | • recognise that there is a degree of uncertainty about the outcome of some events and other events are certain or impossible. | | | | | | | | | | | | ○ | |
| 14:3a | • place events in order of 'likelihood' and use appropriate words to identify them. | | | | | | | | | | | | | ◡ |

◡   Signifies that the chapter partly covers or leads towards the Statement of Attainment.

The use of materials in practical tasks and real life problems (Attainment Targets 1 and 9) is built into the philosophy of the scheme throughout the *Nuffield Maths Teachers' Handbooks*, *Bronto Books* and *Challengers* series.

**Pupils' Record Sheet 3**

Chapters in Teachers' Handbook Two

| AT:Level | Statement of attainment | 1 | 2 | 3 | 4 | 5 | 6 | 7 | 8 | 9 | 10 | 11 | 12 | 13 | 14 | 15 | 16 | 17 | 18 | 19 | 20 | 21 | 22 | 23 | 24 | 25 |
|---|---|---|---|---|---|---|---|---|---|---|---|---|---|---|---|---|---|---|---|---|---|---|---|---|---|---|
| 2:2a | • read, write and order numbers to at least 100; use the knowledge that the tens-digit indicates the number of tens. | ○ | | | | | | | | | | | | | | | | | | | | | | | | |
| 2:2b | • understand the meaning of 'a half' and 'a quarter'. | | | | | | | | | | | | | | | | | | | ○ | | | | | | |
| 2:3b | • use decimal notation as the conventional way of recording in money. | | | | | | | | | | | | | | | | ○ | | | | | | | | | |
| 2:4a | • read, write and order whole numbers. | | | | | | | | | | | | | | | ○ | | | ○ | | | | | | | |
| 2:4d | • recognise and understand simple everyday fractions. | | | | | ○ | | | | | | | | | | | | | | | | | | | | |
| 2:4f | • understand and use the relationship between place values in whole numbers. | | | D | | | | | | | | | | | | | | | | | | | | | | |
| 3:1 | • add or subtract, using objects where the numbers involved are no greater than 10. | ○ | | | | | | | | | | | | | | | | | | | | | | | | |
| 3:3b | • solve problems involving multiplication or division of whole numbers or money, using a calculator where necessary. | | | | | | | | | ○ | | | ○ | | | | ○ | | | ○ | | | | | | |
| 3:3c | • know and use multiplication facts up to 5 × 5, and know all those in the 2, 5 and 10 multiplication tables. | | | | | | | | | ○ | | | ○ | | | | | | | | | | | | | |
| 3:4b | • (using whole numbers) add or subtract mentally two 2-digit numbers; add mentally several single-digit numbers; without a calculator add and subtract two 3-digit numbers, multiply a 2-digit number by a single-digit number and divide a 2-digit number by a single-digit number. | | | | | D | | D | | D | | | D | | | D | | D | | D | | | | | | |
| 4:3a | • recognise that the first digit is the most important in indicating the size of a number, and approximate to the nearest 10 or 100. | | | D | | | | | | | | | | | | | | | | | | | | | | |
| 4:3b | • understand 'remainders' given the context of calculation, and know whether to round up or down. | | | | | | | | | | | | | | | ○ | | | | | | | | | | |
| 5:2b | • distinguish between odd and even numbers. | | | | | | | | | | | | | | | | | | | | | | | | | |
| 5:3a | • explain number patterns and predict subsequent numbers where approximate. | | | | | ○ | | | | | | | | | | | | | | | | | | | | |
| 5:3b | • find number patterns and equivalent forms of 2-digit numbers and use these to perform mental calculations. | | | | | ○ | | | | | | | | | | | | | | | | | | | | |
| 5:3c | • recognise whole numbers which are exactly divisible by 2, 5 and 10. | | | | | | | | | ○ | | | | | | | ○ | | | ○ | | | | | | |
| 5:4a | • apply strategies, such as doubling and halving to explore properties of numbers, including equivalence of fractions. | | | | | | | | | | | | | | | | | | D | | | | | | | |

*Pupils' Record Sheet 3 continued*

Chapters in Teachers' Handbook Two

| AT:Level | Statement of attainment | 1 | 2 | 3 | 4 | 5 | 6 | 7 | 8 | 9 | 10 | 11 | 12 | 13 | 14 | 15 | 16 | 17 | 18 | 19 | 20 | 21 | 22 | 23 | 24 | 25 |
|---|---|---|---|---|---|---|---|---|---|---|---|---|---|---|---|---|---|---|---|---|---|---|---|---|---|---|
| 5:4b | generalise, mainly in words, patterns which arise in various situations. | | | | | | | | | | | | | | | | O | | | | | | | | | |
| 6:2 | understand the use of a symbol to stand for an unknown number. | | | | | O | | O | | O | | | | | | | | | | | | | | | | |
| 6:3 | deal with inputs to and outputs from simple function machines. | | | | | O | | | | | | | | | | O | | | | | | | | | | |
| 7:4 | know the conventions of the coordinate representation of points; work with coordinates in the first quadrant. | | | | | | | | | | | | | D | | | | | | | | | | | | |
| 8:2b | know how to use coins in simple contexts. | | | | | | O | | | | | | | | | | | | | | | | | | | |
| 8:2c | know the most commonly used units in length, capacity, 'weight' and time, and what they are used for. | | | | | | | | | | O | | | | | | | | O | | | | | | | |
| 8:3a | use a wider range of metric units. | | | | O | | | | O | | | | | | | | | O | | | | | O | | O | |
| 8:3b | choose and use appropriate units and instruments in a variety of situations, interpreting numbers on a range of measuring instruments. | | | | | | | | | | O | | | | | | | | | | | | | | | |
| 8:3c | make estimates based on familiar units. | | | | O | | | | | | | | | | | | | | | | | | | | | |
| 8:4a | understand the relationship between units. | | | | | | | | | | | | | | | | | O | O | | | | | | O | |
| 8:4b | find areas by counting squares, and volumes by counting cubes, using whole numbers. | | | | | | | | | | | | | | | | | | | | | | | O | | |
| 10:2a | recognise squares, rectangles, circles, triangles, hexagons, pentagons, cubes, rectangular boxes (cuboids), cylinders and spheres, and describe them. | | | | O | | | | | | | | | | | | | | | | | | | | | |
| 10:3 | sort 2-D and 3-D shapes in different ways and gives reasons for each method of sorting. | | | | | | | | | | | | | | D | | | | | | | | | | | |
| 10:4b | construct simple 2-D and 3-D shapes from given information and know associated language. | | O | | | | | | | | | | | | O | | | | | | | | | | | |
| 11:3a | recognise the (reflective) symmetry in a variety of shapes in 2 and 3 dimensions. | | O | | | | | | | | | | | | O | | | | | | | | | | | |
| 11:4a | specify location by means of coordinates (in the first quadrant) and by means of angle and distance. | | | | | | | | | | | | | D | | | | | | | | | | | | |
| 12:1 | select criteria for sorting a set of objects and apply consistently. | | O | | O | | | | | | | | | | | | | | | | | | | | | |

*Pupils' Record Sheet 3 continued*

### Chapters in Teachers' Handbook Two

| AT:Level | Statement of attainment | 1 | 2 | 3 | 4 | 5 | 6 | 7 | 8 | 9 | 10 | 11 | 12 | 13 | 14 | 15 | 16 | 17 | 18 | 19 | 20 | 21 | 22 | 23 | 24 | 25 |
|---|---|---|---|---|---|---|---|---|---|---|---|---|---|---|---|---|---|---|---|---|---|---|---|---|---|---|
| 12:3 | • extract specific pieces of information from tables and lists. | | | | | ○ | | | | | | | | | | ○ | | | | | | | | | | |
| 13:2a | • construct, read and interpret block graphs and frequency tables. | | | | ○ | | ○ | ○ | ○ | | | ○ | | | | | | | | | | | ○ | | | |
| 13:3a | • construct and interpret bar charts. | | | | ○ | | | | ○ | | | | | | | | | | | | | | | ○ | | |
| 14:3a | • place words in order of 'likelihood' and use appropriate words to identify the chance. | | | | | | | | | | | | | | | | | | | | | | | | | ○ |
| 14:3b | • understand and use the idea of 'evens' and say whether events are more or less likely than this. | | | | | | | | | | | | | | | | | | | | | | | | | ○ |
| 14:3c | • distinguish between 'fair' and 'unfair'. | | | | | | | | | | | | | | | | | | | | | | | | | ○ |

○   Signifies that the chapter partly covers or leads towards the Statement of Attainment.

The use of materials in practical tasks and real life problems (Attainment Targets 1 and 9) is built into the philosophy of the scheme throughout the *Nuffield Maths Teachers' Handbooks*, *Bronto Books* and *Challengers* series.

## Pupils' Record Sheet 2

| Name | Date | Chapters in Teachers' Handbook Two | | | | | | | | | | | | |
|---|---|---|---|---|---|---|---|---|---|---|---|---|---|---|
| AT:Level | Statement of attainment | 1 | 2 | 3 | 4 | 5 | 6 | 7 | 8 | 9 | 10 | 11 | 12 | 13 |
| 2:2a | • read, write and order numbers to at least 100; use the knowledge that the tens-digit indicates the number of tens. | | ⌣ | | | | | | | | | | | |
| 2:2b | • understand the meaning of 'a half' and 'a quarter'. | | | | | | | ○ | | ○ | ○ | | ○ | |
| 2:4d | • recognise and understand everyday fractions. | | | | | | | ⌣ | | ⌣ | ⌣ | | ⌣ | |
| 2:4f | • understand and use the relationship between place values in whole numbers. | | ○ | | | | | | | | | | | |
| 3:2a | • know and use addition and subtraction facts up to 10. | ⌣ | | | | | | | | | | | | |
| 3:2b | • compare two numbers and find the difference. | ○ | | | | | | | | | | | | |
| 3:2c | • solve whole number problems involving addition and subtraction, including money. | | | ○ | ○ | | | | | | | ○ | | |
| 3:3a | • know and use addition and subtraction facts up to 20 (including zero). | | | ○ | ○ | | | | | | | | | |
| 3:3b | • solve problems involving multiplication or division of whole numbers or money; using a calculator where necessary. | | | | | ○ | ○ | | | | | | | |
| 3:3c | • know and use multiplication facts up to 5 × 5, and all those in 2, 5 and 10 multiplication tables. | | | | | ○ | | | | | | | | |
| 4:2 | • make a sensible estimate of a number of objects up to 20. | | | ○ | | | | | | | | | | |
| 4:3a | • recognise that the first digit is the most important in indicating the size of a number, and approximate to the nearest 10 or 100. | | ⌣ | | | | | | | | | | | |
| 4:3b | • understand 'remainders' given the context of calculation, and know whether to round up or down. | | | | | | ⌣ | | | | | | | |
| 5:1 | • copy, continue and devise repeating patterns represented by objects/apparatus or one-digit numbers. | | | ○ | | | | | | | | | | |
| 5:2a | • explore and use the patterns in addition and subtraction facts to 10. | ○ | | | | | | | | | | ○ | | |
| 5:3a | • explain number patterns and predict subsequent numbers where appropriate. | | | | ○ | ○ | | | | | | | | |
| 6:2 | • understand the use of a symbol to stand for an unknown number. | | | | ○ | | | | | | | | | |
| 8:2a | • use non-standard measures in length, area, volume, capacity, weight and time to compare objects and recognise the need to use standard units. | | | | | | | ○ | | ○ | ○ | | ○ | |
| 8:2b | • know how to use coins in simple contexts. | | | | | | | | | | | ○ | | |
| 8:2c | • know the most commonly used units in length, capacity, weight and time, and what they are used for. | | | | | | | ○ | | ○ | ○ | | ○ | |
| 8:3a | • use a wider range of metric units. | | | | | | | ○ | | ○ | | | ○ | |

Recording progress:   ⊘  ⌣   denotes pupil has **started**
                      ⊗  ⌣   denotes pupil has **covered**
                      ⊗  ⌣   denotes pupil has **understood**

Longman